MORE READING POWER

TEST BOOKLET

BEATRICE S. MIKULECKY / LINDA JEFFRIES

Longman

More Reading Power Test Booklet

Pearson Education, 10 Bank Street, White Plains, NY 10606

Vice president, director of publishing: Allen Ascher
Editorial director: Louisa Hellegers
Acquisitions editor: Laura Le Dréan
Senior development manager: Penny Laporte
Vice president, director of design and production: Rhea Banker
Development editor: Andrew Gitzy
Production manager: Alana Zdinak
Production supervisor: Liza Pleva
Executive managing editor: Linda Moser
Production editor: Lynn Contrucci
Director of manufacturing: Patrice Fraccio
Senior manufacturing buyer: Dave Dickey
Interior design adaptation: DePinho Graphic Design
Composition: ElectraGraphics, Inc.

Text credits: **Pages 8–9, 47–48:** From the *Encyclopedia Americana,* 1997 Edition. Copyright
© 1997 by Grolier Incorporated. Reprinted with permission from the publisher. **Page 10:**
From "Timed Readings, Book Eight" by Edward Spargo, © 1989. Used with permission of
NTC/Contemporary Publishing Group, Inc. **Page 19:** From *Raise the Issues* by Carol Numrich.
Copyright © 1994 by Longman Inc. Reprinted with permission from the publisher. **Page 52:**
From the "Hitch-hiker" in THE WONDERFUL WORLD OF HENRY SUGAR AND SIX MORE by
Roald Dahl. Copyright © 1945, 1947, 1952, 1977 by Roald Dahl. Reprinted by permission of
Alfred A. Knopf Children's Books, a division of Random House, Inc. (US) and from Jonathan
Cape Ltd. and Penguin Books Ltd. (UK). **Page 53:** © 1972 Judith Chernaik. Reprinted with
permission. **Page 54:** Reprinted with permission from Barbara Thompson Davis—the trustee
of the Katherine Anne Porter Estate. **Pages 49–51:** From "Chimpanzee" by Duane M.
Rumbaugh, *The World Book Encyclopedia,* 1996 Edition. Copyright © 1996 by World Book, Inc.
Reprinted with permission.

ISBN 0-13-018649-X

1 2 3 4 5 6 7 8 9 10—DPC—05 04 03 02 01 00

Contents

Introduction

More Reading Power Student Book is divided into four parts: Part One: *Reading for Pleasure,* Part Two: *Reading Comprehension Skills,* Part Three: *Thinking Skills,* and Part Four: *Reading Faster.* This booklet includes tests for Part Two and Part Three. No formal tests for Part One and Part Four are included because the skills developed in these parts are not amenable to group testing. However, the booklet does offer a variety of ideas and activities for evaluating these aspects of reading development on an individual basis.

Some of the later exercises in each unit of the Student Book can also be used to evaluate student progress. Teachers who decide to use those exercises for that purpose should have students remove the Answer Key from the back of their books (pages 275–289) at the beginning of the semester. These pages have been perforated for easy removal. The Answer Key can be stapled and collected. Teachers can then redistribute them on occasions when students need to check their own answers.

If you would like to read more about the teaching of reading, we suggest the following texts:

Brown, D. *A World of Books: An Annotated Reading List for ESL/EFL Students,* TESOL, 1988.

Brown, D. *Books for a Small Planet: A Multicultural-Intercultural Bibliography for Young English Language Learners,* TESOL, 1994.

Carter, R., and M. McCarthy. *Vocabulary and Language Teaching,* Longman, 1988.

Day, R. (ed.). *New Ways in Teaching Reading,* TESOL, 1993.

Day, R., and J. Bamford. *Extensive Reading in the Second Language Classroom,* Cambridge University Press, 1998.

Mikulecky, B. *A Short Course in Teaching Reading Skills,* Addison Wesley Longman, 1990.

Part One

Evaluating Reading for Pleasure

Before starting work in Reading for Pleasure, teachers are strongly urged to read the teacher's notes for this section on pages 291–293 in the Teacher's Guide at the end of the Student Book. In these pages, teachers will find both practical suggestions for organizing reading for pleasure in class, and an explanation of the rationale and objectives of this part of the book. Also included are some ideas for evaluating students' progress in their pleasure-reading books, which are expanded on here.

There are a number of reasons to evaluate students' progress in the Reading for Pleasure section. First of all, teachers may need to verify that students have read what they say they have read. Teachers may also be required by the school to provide an assessment of the students' work. From the students' point of view, the fact that teachers spend classroom time on evaluation or follow-up activities encourages students to take their reading for pleasure more seriously. Furthermore, activities that involve sharing the reading experience with other students can provide additional opportunities for practice in speaking and writing.

Teachers should be careful, however, not to overdo follow-up activities and so take all the pleasure out of pleasure reading. Students who are often required to follow up their reading with tedious exercises may come to dread finishing a book. Many exercises may seem like "busy work" to students, without relevance to them and their reading experience. In fact, outside the classroom when people talk or write about books, they usually focus only on their reaction to the book; they examine their own personal response and share that response with others. The same should be true in the classroom. The activities proposed here try to adhere to this principle.

One further note of caution: ***Teachers need to keep in mind the real purpose of reading for pleasure (also known as extensive reading), which is to encourage students to read as much as possible.*** However valid a follow-up activity, it cannot replace the reading itself. Teachers must take care not to allow these follow-up evaluation activities to take up classroom or homework time that could be spent reading.

1 Oral activities for evaluation

Book conferences

As mentioned in the Teacher's Guide, these brief conversations with individual students about their books can provide valuable feedback on students' reading. With the teacher's questions as a model for the kind of language to use, students also develop their ability to engage in discussions about books and ideas.

Book discussion groups

As an alternative or in addition to the individual conferences, teachers can organize regular book discussions in pairs or small groups—not more than four students. The following are some general guidelines for book discussion groups:

1. Groups can be formed randomly or according to shared reading interests (e.g., a group of students who love thrillers).
2. In each discussion session, students report in turn on their progress in reading their book.
3. The reports should be brief—not more than two or three minutes—and informal, with no written preparation.
4. To prevent students from speaking for too long, one student in each group could be given the job of timing the others.
5. To ensure that all members are listening, each group member could be required to ask a question after a student has finished talking.
6. Students should be told not to summarize the plot, and especially not to reveal the ending, but rather to speak about their reactions to the book. These discussions can lead to students' exchanging books when they have finished reading them.

While these discussions are going on, the teacher can circulate and listen in or comment on the students' views or reactions. The teacher may not be able to hear every student during one discussion session, but if the groups meet frequently, teachers will be able to get a good idea of how the students are progressing.

Book talks

As mentioned in the Teacher's Guide, a good way for the teacher to inform students about books is to give "book talks" to the class. These should be short and personal, and should convey enthusiasm for the book. In these talks, teachers give a brief introduction to a book's content and a general reaction to various aspects of the book such as character, mood, and the author's intentions. After a few of these talks, the teacher can then ask students to give similar talks, either in front of the whole class or in smaller groups.

Students who are less confident about their oral skills may work better with a skeleton outline to help them. For example:

Introduction: Title and author
                     Type of book (e.g., mystery)
                     Length and difficulty
Body: What I liked about the book and why (characters, mood, setting, style, subject matter, a favorite passage)
                     What I did not like about the book, if anything
Conclusion: I recommend/don't recommend this book

2 *Written activities for evaluation*

Record of books read

On page 9 of *More Reading Power* Student Book, students can write down basic information about the books that they have read. A frequent look at this list will allow teachers to get some idea of what students are reading. Any doubts about whether a student has really read all the books on his/her list may be dispelled with a few quick questions about the books.

The idea of keeping a "record of books read" can be expanded to include a sentence or two with the reader's opinion. These opinions can be shared with the rest of the class to give others ideas about which books they might enjoy. There are several ways to organize this. One way is to ask students to fill out a note card with basic information and a brief opinion after they finish a book (as in the Book Response Sheet on page 10 of the Student Book). These note cards can then be kept on file in the classroom, to be consulted by students looking for reading suggestions. Alternatively, the book responses could be kept in a binder, with a page for each book on which students note their opinions.

Book reviews

Teachers should avoid the classic book report that simply summarizes a book. These reports are uninteresting to write and to read. Teachers can assign a different kind of report, however, in which students write about one or two aspects of their personal reaction to a book. Students can be given a list of possibilities from which to choose one or two to write about. The following list is adapted from Day and Bamford (p. 143):

• Characters that students identify with
• Points of the story or behavior that interest students
• Personal experiences or thoughts related to the book
• Favorite parts of the book
• Parts of the book or characters that students dislike
• Larger issues dealt with or raised by the book (e.g. war, sexism)

In order to complete this kind of assignment, students will need to know some of the basic conventions for writing in English, including paragraph formation and simple essay form (introduction, body, and conclusion). The teacher can respond to the student, either by commenting on the student's reaction or, if the teacher has read the book, by giving his/her own reaction. Aside from being more stimulating to write and read, these reaction reports have an advantage over the traditional book report: It is difficult, if not impossible, for a student to invent a reaction without having read the book.

The concept of writing opinions about books can be extended to include book reviews for a classroom newsletter or for a newsletter put together for the whole English-language program.

Student-generated comprehension questions

In the traditional reading classroom, students are often asked to respond to comprehension questions at the end of a reading. For students, this task often becomes mechanical, and again has little relation to their reading experience. These exercises can be made more relevant by asking questions about the reader's understanding of the author's intentions, or about the reader's reaction to some aspect of the text.

For working on pleasure reading, however, there is another problem with teacher-generated comprehension questions. Since the students are all reading different books, which the teacher may or may not have read, it is not easy to come up with questions for each book. The solution to this problem could be to ask students to write their own questions. Before doing this, they need some guidance about what kinds of questions are appropriate and how to write them.

If students have had at least one book conference with the teacher, they will be familiar with the types of questions that are appropriate. The best questions for pleasure reading are not literal questions that test for memory of specific facts about the book, but elaborative questions that allow students to elaborate on the book and deepen their own awareness of it. The following list is taken from Mikulecky: *A Short Course in Teaching Reading Skills,* pp. 19–20.

Elaborative question types

Expressive	How did you like the book?
Factual	Who is the main character? Where is the story set?
Informational	What was it about?
Experiential	Did anything like that ever happen to you?
Affective	How did that make you feel?
Relational	Did you ever hear of anything like this in your country (or neighborhood)?
Critical	Do you think that this could really happen?
Predictive	What do you think will happen next
Stylistic	Did the author do a good job in making that character seem real?
Sequential	What happened after that?
Cause/Effect	What made the tree fall into the road?
Summarizing	Can you tell the whole story in just a few sentences?
Speculative	What would this story be like if someone else were telling the story?
Inferential	Why do you think a character behaved as she/he did in that situation?

Predictions about books

Predictions can be used for several purposes. First, asking students who are part-way through a book to predict how they think it will end stimulates them to reflect on what they are reading and to use their imagination. It is also another way for teachers to show interest in students' reading and to measure students' progress. Students can write down their predictions for the teacher to collect and then hand back when the book has been finished. Students can then compare what they predicted with the actual ending.

Following this activity, students could write about their reactions to the actual ending of their book and whether or not they liked it. They can then be asked to imagine and write about an alternative ending, or even a sequel if they think the book could be continued.

3 Negotiated evaluations

One further possibility teachers may want to consider, depending on their teaching contexts, is to allow students to decide together how they would prefer to have their reading evaluated. Dupuy, Tse, and Cook suggest that this "can be quite liberating for both the teacher and the student. Also, in this way, the process of creating independent readers—from choosing their own books to evaluating their own reading progress—is complete" (p. 14).

Furthermore, "students choosing their own evaluation are more likely to select projects that are interesting and meaningful to them, and in turn, give a more accurate demonstration of their ability and proficiency than standardized or imposed evaluations" (p. 14). Contrary to what some teachers might expect, students do not generally choose easy assignments for themselves, but tend to take this responsibility quite seriously. Teachers might need to start by presenting some oral or written options. Dupuy, Tse, and Cook (p. 14) list the following examples of student-generated evaluation projects:

Creating mock news broadcasts or news reports of selected events in the stories
Writing a "diary" of one or more characters
Forming book-promotion teams to introduce books to other classes
Writing sequels to stories or books
Creating comic books or simplified versions of a book for less proficient students to read

Further reading

Day, R., and J. Bamford. *Extensive Reading in the Second Language Classroom*, Cambridge University Press, New York, 1998.

Dupuy, B., L. Tse, and T. Cook. "Bringing Books into the Classroom: First Steps in Turning College-Level ESL Students into Readers," *TESOL Journal*, Summer 1996.

Mikulecky, B. S. *A Short Course in Teaching Reading Skills*, Addison Wesley Longman, White Plains, NY, 1990.

Part Two

Evaluating Reading Comprehension Skills

In *More Reading Power*, reading comprehension is viewed as a thinking process and reading comprehension skills are seen as they fit into that process. This approach is explained in detail on page 293 of the Teacher's Guide in the Student Book and in *A Short Course in Teaching Reading Skills,* by Beatrice S. Mikulecky. The reading comprehension skills units in the Student Book are designed to make students consciously aware of the thinking process that good readers of English employ while they are reading. It is this awareness, together with practice in the specific skills, that will allow students to improve their comprehension.

Research has shown that a test best measures the level of mastery of a skill or trait when the test reflects the format of the training. Therefore, the tests on comprehension skills in this booklet are very similar in format to the exercises in each unit. The approach teachers take to the responses of their students should also be similar. In all of these activities, a primary aim is to lead students to explore their thinking processes and to open a "window" through which teacher and student can examine those processes. Since no two students think exactly alike, these responses may often differ; their responses may not coincide exactly with the answer given in the Answer Key. This is true of both the exercises and the tests. The Answer Key should be taken as an indication of a possible answer, but any responses that students can reasonably justify should be accepted.

In some of the unit tests, students are explicitly asked to explain their thinking as part of the test. For students, this task will be simply an extension of what they have been doing in class, since many of the skills exercises require students to work together, talk about their choices, and explain their reasoning. Furthermore, as recommended in the Teacher's Guide, teachers should continually be asking students how they came up with their answers and what they were thinking. Thus, students should have developed the ability to internalize or "talk to themselves" about their thinking. The tests merely ask them to put this in writing.

Scoring the tests which ask for explanations will require more time and effort on the part of the teacher, since it will be necessary to read the individual student's responses and evaluate the thinking behind them. However, doing this will allow the teacher to get a more accurate sense of each student's progress than would otherwise be possible. It should also be noted that the responsibility and extra time involved are not so different from what is required of a teacher of composition who aims to lead students to a better understanding of the thinking process required to express themselves clearly in English.

A final note about the reason why there are fewer tests for Units 1, 2, and 8 (Scanning, Previewing and Predicting, and Skimming): The skills practiced in these units can be further practiced and/or evaluated in other parts of the book, such as in Unit 7: Patterns of Organization or in the passages in Part Four: Reading Faster.

Unit 1: **Scanning**

Test 1

➤ **You are writing a report about chimpanzees and you find this entry from The Encyclopedia Americana—International Edition. Scan the entry to find the answers to the questions. Work quickly! Time limit: 5 minutes.**

1. In which parts of Africa are chimpanzees found? _____

2. How tall is the average chimpanzee? _____

3. How much does a newborn chimpanzee weigh? _____

4. How long can a chimpanzee live? _____

5. How many chimpanzees live together in a band? _____

6. Where do chimpanzees spend most of their time each day? _____

7. What do chimpanzees eat? _____

8. How do chimpanzees express excitement? _____

9. What separates the different races of chimpanzees? _____

10. How do chimpanzees show their intelligence? _____

_____

CHIMPANZEE, chim-pan-'zē, a great ape native to the dense forests and open woodlands of west and central equatorial Africa. The common chimpanzee is classified as a single species, *Pan troglodytes*, but there is as much variation among chimpanzees as among men. The pigmy chimpanzee is considered by many authorities to be a distinct species, *Pan paniscus*. Chimpanzees are highly intelligent social animals closely related to man, and for this reason they are valuable for use in medical and behavioral research.

Characteristics. Adult chimpanzees have few natural enemies other than disease, for they are large, powerfully built animals that stand about 4.5 feet (1.3 meters) high and weigh an average of 115 pounds (52 kilograms). There are wide individual differences, and the male tends to be somewhat larger and more robust than the female.

The gestation period of the chimpanzee is 7 months, and the newborn animal weighs about 4 pounds (1.8 kilograms). It is almost as helpless as a human infant. It clutches the hair on its mother's sides and back while it clings to her chest and stomach. Only the head has any appreciable amount of black hair at birth; there is a white tuft at the anal region, and another is often found at the chin. The hair tends to lighten with age, whereas the skin darkens. Some individuals develop black faces early in life, but others only develop a tan face color.

As the infant chimpanzee grows, it begins to explore the world; it starts to ride on the mother's back when she travels. A new infant is seldom born before the last one is two or three years old. Even at that age the juvenile chimpanzee remains closely associated with its mother, although it spends more and more time with its playmates and other members of its band. The chimpanzee reaches full stature at about age 12; few achieve the potential life-span of over 50.

Behavior. A band of chimpanzees, which usually contains 6 to 10 members, exists as part of a larger community of bands. These bands may exchange members, merge, or divide, depending on available foods and other factors. Some bands consist only of adult males or of mothers and young, but individuals appear to come and go freely within the community.

Much of the life of the chimpanzees is spent in the trees, where they sleep and obtain the fruits that constitute the bulk of their diet. They also eat other vegetable matter and insects, and there are reliable reports of chimpanzees killing and eating small mammals. The apes seldom venture far from trees, and they avoid direct sunlight. A sleeping nest is built each night, and a resting platform may be built during the day.

The chimpanzee's long arms are suited to brachiation (swinging through trees), but most purposeful travel takes place on the ground. Chimpanzees walk on the soles of the feet and the middle phalanges of the flexed fingers. A chimpanzee can also stand erect on its short stocky legs. Some individuals may travel short distances on their legs

only, especially when the hands are being used to carry an object. When excited, males often stand on their legs and also put on an impressive display. The display usually starts with swaying or stamping and with vocal sounds that reach a crescendo scream. This may be followed either with a final charge or the flinging of objects, or both. These displays, however, seldom express directed aggression.

Chimpanzees do not swim. Therefore the major rivers in the rain forests where they live may be effective barriers separating the different races of chimpanzees.

Intelligence. Chimpanzees are very responsive and easily excited animals, and they enter into many tasks with great exuberance. They display great versatility in the range of problems they can solve and in their ability to manipulate objects and fashion crude tools. Although their performance on particular tasks may be matched by some monkeys, no monkey tested has been able to equal the versatility of the chimpanzee.

Young chimpanzees often become strongly attached to their trainers, and even adult chimpanzees show partiality to certain people. The chimpanzee is, above all, an intelligent social animal requiring companionship and a sufficiently stimulating environment to keep it active and interested in life.

Chimpanzees are classified in the family Pongidae, suborder Anthropoidea, order Primates.

IRWIN S. BERNSTEIN
Yerkes Regional Primate Center
Emory University

Further reading: Ghiglieri, M., *East of the Mountains of the Moon* (Free Press, 1987); Goodall, Jane, *The Chimpanzees of Gombe* (Harvard University Press, 1986).

Unit 2: **Previewing and Predicting**

Test 1

➤ *Preview this article and predict what it is about. Time limit: 30 seconds to preview. Then answer the questions on the next page.*

A Token of Peace

Many romantic legends have been inspired by Sacagawea, the Shoshone Indian woman who accompanied Lewis and Clark on much of their expedition of 1804–1806.

One of President Jefferson's major purposes in commissioning Lewis and Clark to explore the newly acquired Louisiana Territory had been the establishing of friendly relations with Indian tribes between St. Louis and the Pacific Ocean. Indian chiefs were to be given Jefferson peace medals at these historic first contacts with white men.

In the winter of 1804, some 1,600 miles from their St. Louis starting point, Lewis and Clark arrived in the North Dakota country of the Mandan Indians, where they were befriended by the tribe and spent a peaceful winter. Living among the Mandans were a French Canadian fur trader, Touissaint Charbonneau, and his young Indian wife, Sacagawea. When the expedition left Mandan country, the couple went with it. Charbonneau was hired as an interpreter for $25 a month and Sacagawea carried her newborn baby on her back.

Sacagawea's main reason for accompanying the explorers was a longing to see her own Shoshone people again. Five years earlier, at the age of 12, she had been stolen by Crow Indians, taken far from her Rocky Mountain home, and sold as a slave to the Missouri River Mandans. In time, she had been sold to Charbonneau.

Sacagawea was of great value to the expedition in her role as peace envoy and intermediary with Indian tribes. Clark said of her, "Sacagawea reconciles all the Indians to our friendly intentions. A woman with a party of men is a token of peace."

Across the Missouri River, Lewis and Clark were faced with the snow-capped Rocky Mountains. Crossing them would be impossible without horses. Going on ahead, Lewis met a band of Shoshone Indians, and persuaded them to return with him to the expedition. With the tremendous advantage of Sacagawea's relationship, the explorers were able to barter for 29 Shoshone horses, and the journey continued.

Across the Rockies, the party built canoes and followed the Columbia River to the Pacific. The two explorers frequently praised Sacagawea's endurance and fortitude. She must have also been undemanding. Lewis wrote of her, "If she has enough to eat and a few trinkets to wear, I believe she would be perfectly content anywhere." Sacagawea was among those Indians honored with the prized Jefferson peace medal, evidence of the genuine fondness Lewis and Clark felt for her.

➤ **Do not look back at the article. There is no time limit on this part.**

Answer the questions.

1. What is the article about? _____

_____

2. What are some dates and/or other numbers you noticed while previewing? _____

_____

3. What are some names mentioned in the article? _____

_____

4. What are some places mentioned in the article? _____

_____

Recalling Facts

Choose the best ending for each sentence.

5. The president who commissioned Lewis and Clark was
   - ❑ a. Jefferson.
   - ❑ b. Madison.
   - ❑ c. Jackson.

6. By the winter of 1804, Lewis and Clark had traveled about
   - ❑ a. 500 miles.
   - ❑ b. 1,000 miles.
   - ❑ c. 1,500 miles.

7. Charbonneau was hired as an interpreter at a monthly salary of
   - ❑ a. $25.
   - ❑ b. $100.
   - ❑ c. $175.

8. Clark considered the presence of a woman in a group of men to be a
   - ❑ a. token of peace.
   - ❑ b. sign of good luck.
   - ❑ c. guarantee against attack.

9. The author mentions that Lewis and Clark crossed the
   - ❑ a. Mississippi River.
   - ❑ b. Missouri River.
   - ❑ c. Columbia River.

Understanding the Passage

Choose the best ending for each sentence.

10. Because of Sacagawea, the expedition was able to
    - ❑ a. trade items for horses.
    - ❑ b. find a lost Indian tribe.
    - ❑ c. build canoes.

11. Sacagawea is described as a
    - ❑ a. self-centered leader.
    - ❑ b. tireless person.
    - ❑ c. creative individual.

12. The author suggests that Sacagawea
    - ❑ a. is an important figure in American history.
    - ❑ b. was a personal friend of the president.
    - ❑ c. was not an Indian by birth.

13. The president wanted Lewis and Clark to give the Indians
    - ❑ a. parcels of land in the newly acquired territory.
    - ❑ b. small amounts of American money.
    - ❑ c. symbolic pieces of jewelry.

14. Sacagawea traveled with Lewis and Clark because she
    - ❑ a. was well paid for her work.
    - ❑ b. was needed as an interpreter.
    - ❑ c. wanted to visit her original tribe.

Unit 3: Vocabulary Knowledge for Effective Reading

❖ Guessing meaning from context in sentences

Test 1

➤ *In each of the following items, there is a word you may not know. Guess the meaning of the word from the context of the sentences. Write the meaning on the line.*

1. What does "novice" mean? _____
   - George was no longer a novice at the computer. Though he had only been using it for a short time, he could already use many of the programs.
   - Because she was a novice swimmer, she was not allowed to go into the deep water.

2. What does "succinct" mean? _____
   - The doctor needed only a few words to describe his patient. His succinct comment was, "Nothing wrong here."
   - Suzanne's teachers were very succinct in their report to Suzanne's parents. They had simply written, "A model student."

3. What does "frugal" mean? _____
   - As a student, Suhan had very little extra money, so he had to be very frugal with his spending.
   - My grandmother was a frugal housewife. She was able to keep her house nice and make delicious meals with very little money.

4. What does "saw" mean? _____
   - After we cut down the tree, we'll saw it into logs for the fireplace.
   - Suki worked hard to make a bookshelf. First, she had to saw the wood into pieces. Then she put the pieces together and nailed them in place.

5. What does "skull" mean? _____
   - From the animal's skull, scientists could tell the shape of its head and the size of its brain.
   - Near the wolves' old home, we found the whitened bones and skulls of many small animals, but no signs that wolves were still living there.

6. What does "ooze" mean? _____
   - When Jill stepped into the lake, the mud oozed around her bare toes.
   - No one liked the pizza that Gianni made because he had used too much oil. In fact, oil was oozing off the pizza and all over our plates.

Unit 3:   Vocabulary Knowledge
for Effective Reading

❖ Guessing meaning from context in sentences

Test 2

➤ *In each of the following items, there is a word you may not know. Guess the meaning of the word from the context of the sentences. Write the meaning on the line.*

1. What does "quarry" mean? _____
   - Stone from the quarry in Stonington, Maine, was used to build many famous buildings, such as the Museum of Fine Arts in Boston.
   - In the late 1900s, many men came from Italy to work in the Stonington quarry. These men already had a lot of experience cutting out stone in Italian quarries.

2. What does "go sour" mean? _____
   - If you leave milk out of the refrigerator all day, it will go sour.
   - The milk in her cup had a terrible smell. It had definitely gone sour, so she didn't drink it.

3. What does "usher" mean? _____
   - The usher at the theater had a small flashlight, so he could show us to our seats in the dark.
   - After she finished high school, Judy got a job as an usher at the local movie theater. The job was boring, but she got to see lots of movies.

4. What does "haggle" mean? _____
   - In some countries, shopkeepers normally have high prices for their goods. They expect customers to haggle over those prices, and then they will agree to a lower price.
   - Darek had a bad day at work today. He was haggling with his boss about an increase in pay.

5. What does "breed" mean? _____
   - My friend Tom wants to move to the country and breed dogs. He says you can make a lot of money selling certain kinds of dogs.
   - There's a farm down the road where they breed race horses. Every spring we see the most beautiful young horses out with their mothers.

6. What does "aboard" mean? _____
   - The captain yelled, "All aboard!" and everyone rushed to get on the boat before it left.
   - There were 1,200 people aboard the *Titanic* when it hit an iceberg and sank.

Unit 3: Vocabulary Knowledge for Effective Reading

❖ **Guessing meaning from context in sentences**

Test 3

➤ *In each of the following items, there is a word you may not know. Guess the meaning of the word from the context of the sentences. Write the meaning on the line.*

1. What does "blissful" mean? _____
   - It was a blissful moment when Julie said she would marry me. I had never felt so happy in my life.
   - "How was your weekend?" asked Salim. "Blissful," said Ajar. "I did nothing all day except lie in the sun."

2. What does "stray" mean? _____
   - Jimmy found a stray cat in the village. No one wanted it. The poor thing was so thin and sad-looking, we decided to bring it home and keep it.
   - Stray cats and dogs can sometimes be a problem. Since they don't belong to anyone and they are not cared for, they can carry diseases.

3. What does "leak" mean? _____
   - I think there's a leak in this milk container. There's milk all over the refrigerator.
   - Last week I discovered that the roof had a leak. There was a terrible storm and water was dripping right over my bed!

4. What does "blister" mean? _____
   - After two hours of walking in his new shoes, Jordie had a blister on the back of one foot.
   - It's hard work digging a hole to plant a tree. By the time I finished, I had blisters on both hands.

5. What does "mutter" mean? _____
   - Mr. Richards muttered something angrily to himself, but I couldn't hear what he said.
   - I often hear our neighbor muttering to herself about my messy yard, but she doesn't dare say anything to me about it.

6. What does "hence" mean? _____
   - The clothes were poor quality, and hence they were not acceptable. We had to send them back.
   - The pay is low and the working conditions are terrible. Hence, I have decided not to take the job.

Unit 3:   Vocabulary Knowledge for Effective Reading

❖ Referents in a longer essay

Test 1

➤ *Read "How the Hawaiian Islands Were Formed" on the next page. Then fill in the table below. Write the referent for each word or words. See the example for line 3.*

Line	Word or words	Referent
3	they	the Hawaiian Islands
6	they	
9	They	
10	This	
11	archipelago	
15	they	
22	it	
22	this volcano	
25	there	
31	evolved	
36	It	

How the Hawaiian Islands Were Formed

1   The formation of the Hawaiian Islands was very different from the formation of the continents. Geologists (scientists who study the earth) believe that the islands appeared separately and more recently. According to the geological evidence, they were formed by volcanoes about 30 million years ago.

5   These volcanoes began when some cracks appeared on the bottom of the Pacific Ocean. Deep under the earth's surface, the rocks are very hot, so hot that they are in a liquid form called lava. This lava can sometimes come up through openings on the surface of the earth. The piles of lava slowly build up and become mountains. When the openings are on the ocean floor, the mountains are at first underwater. They may eventually become tall enough
10   to rise above the water and form islands. This is how the Hawaiian Archipelago was created. This archipelago, or collection of islands, consists of 132 points of land. The larger points of land of the archipelago are the Hawaiian Islands.

According to geologists, the islands in the Hawaiian Archipelago are still changing, like living things. The oldest islands, such as the Kure Atoll, are slowly disappearing under the
15   sea. Over thousands of years, they have gradually been worn down by storms and the ocean waves. Now nothing is left but a semi-circle of coral reef (rock-like forms made by tiny sea animals).

Other, younger islands, however, are still growing. The Big Island of Hawaii has two active volcanoes which are still adding new lava to the island. There are also new islands in
20   the archipelago in the process of formation. Geologists have found an underwater volcano about 30 miles south of the island of Hawaii. Now about 3,000 feet below the surface of the ocean, it will probably rise above the water. Someday, this volcano could become another Hawaiian Island.

The islands at first were bare rock and empty of all life. They remained this way for mil-
25   lions of years. The first kinds of plant life were probably carried there as seeds by the wind or by the ocean. Plants grew well in the rich, volcanic dirt, and birds were attracted to the islands. Birds may then have brought more seeds from faraway places, and so introduced other new plants.

All this took a very long time. Scientists believe that at the most, one new plant arrived
30   every 20,000 years! But slowly the plants and the birds on the islands became more numerous and more varied. They also gradually evolved, changing to adapt themselves to their conditions. That is why the islands are home to so many plants and birds that can be found nowhere else.

The plants on the islands also attracted insects, which may have been blown there by
35   storms. With just a few exceptions, plants, birds, and insects were the only forms of life. Then, about 1,500 years ago, the first humans arrived, bringing other animals with them. It was the beginning of an era of change for the Hawaiian Islands.

Unit 3: Vocabulary Knowledge for Effective Reading

❖ Referents in a longer essay

Test 2

➤ *Read "The Official-English Movement" on the next page. Then fill in the table below. Write the referent for each word or words. See the example for line 6.*

Line	Word or words	Referent
6	they	immigrants
8	they	
8	their	
12	its	
16	they	
18	In this way	
22	their	
23	the nation's	
24	their	
29	it	
32	countries	
39	they	

The Official-English Movement

1   There is a new movement in the United States: the official-English movement. Although most Americans speak English, U.S. lawmakers have never proclaimed English the official national language. Today there are many people who would like to make that proclamation official.

5   In the early nineteenth century, many immigrants of different lands and tongues arrived in the United States; <u>they</u> were expected to learn English right away. Parents sent their children to American schools, where students were immersed in the English language. It was only by learning English that <u>they</u> could get an education and find a job in <u>their</u> new world. Yet, although people were expected to learn English (and generally did), English was never
10   the official language.

       With the more recent growth of a multicultural, multilingual society in the United States, as in other nations of the world, the question of whether or not <u>its</u> population should be required to share a common language has arisen. In order to accommodate the many language groups living in the United States, government agencies, schools, and businesses often
15   offer their services in other languages. For example, when Florida residents go to vote for local or national candidates, <u>they</u> can read their ballots in Spanish. Non-English-speaking schoolchildren, often Hispanic or Chinese, may study in bilingual education programs, in which they are taught in their native language until they master English. <u>In this way</u>, the children are presumed to gain a sense of identity and self-confidence, which will help them
20   succeed in the future.

       Believing that the American people have become disparate with multilingualism and that <u>their</u> common tongue, English, is the only thread that still binds Americans together, many people have proposed making English <u>the nation's</u> official language. In fact, many states have already passed legislation making English <u>their</u> official language. They feel that a com-
25   mon language is the only way to encourage people who have been lumped together to participate fully in the country's democracy. They argue that immigrants cannot be woven into the culture of American society without a common thread, in this case language, and they support their argument by pointing to history: The ancestors of many Americans came to the United States knowing no English but learned <u>it</u> quickly because it was indispensable for
30   their integration; as a result, they became successful and "American." Supporters of making English an official United States language also refer to the examples of Canada and Belgium, <u>countries</u> that have been divided emotionally and politically into two language and cultural groups because of bilingualism.

       Opponents of the official-English movement maintain that requiring all U.S. citizens to
35   speak English deprives non-English-speaking Americans of their basic rights and is a violation of free speech. The opposition feels that official English would not lead to harmony in the United States but rather would promote xenophobia, the fear of foreigners and their cultures. Moreover, they see America as a more vibrant, interesting society because of its multilingual, multicultural composition. Ethnic pluralism, <u>they</u> say, is what has strengthened the United
40   States.

Unit 4: Topics

❖ Working with the topic

Test 1

➤ *Which item does not belong in the list? Think of a topic for each group of words. Write the topic. Cross out the item in each group that does not fit the topic. There may be more than one possible correct answer. On the line below each group of words, explain your answer. Why did you choose that topic? Why did you cross out that item?*

1. Topic: _____

   milk   tea   water   gasoline   vinegar   beer   orange juice

   _____

2. Topic: _____

   Neptune   Pluto   Earth   Venus   Uranus   Mercury   Moon

   _____

3. Topic: _____

   violin   banjo   viola   guitar   clarinet   bass   cello

   _____

4. Topic: _____

   Indonesia   Malaysia   South Korea   Vietnam   Cambodia   Hawaii   Thailand

   _____

5. Topic: _____

   California   Oregon   Washington   New Mexico   Arizona   Nevada   Massachusetts

   _____

6. Topic: _____

   Germany   Italy   Austria   Belgium   France   Canada   Switzerland

   _____

7. Topic: _____

   swimming   hiking   biking   running   jogging   aerobics   walking

   _____

8. Topic: _____

   potatoes   carrots   beets   turnips   cucumbers   radishes

   _____

9. Topic: _____

   Arabic   Flemish   Italian   Swahili   Urdu   American   Spanish

   _____

10. Topic: _____

    Siberia   Alaska   North Pole   South Pole   Canada   Norway   Greenland

    _____

Unit 4: **Topics**

❖ **Working with the topic**

Test 2

➤ *Which item does not belong in the list? Think of a topic for each group of words. Write the topic. Cross out the item in each group that does not fit the topic. There may be more than one possible correct answer. On the line below each group of words, explain your answer. Why did you choose that topic? Why did you cross out that item?*

1. Topic: _____

   president   mayor   governor   prime minister   king   senator

   _____

2. Topic: _____

   sapphire   diamond   ruby   gold   emerald   topaz   opal

   _____

3. Topic: _____

   gloves   twins   shoes   socks   mittens   pants   skates

   _____

4. Topic: _____

   Volkswagen   Honda   Subaru   Volvo   Ford   Toyota   Porsche

   _____

5. Topic: _____

   gruyere   cheddar   vanilla   parmesan   blue   swiss   mozzarella

   _____

6. Topic: _____

   dairy   produce   meat   delicatessen   check-out   bakery

   _____

7. Topic: _____

Paul McCartney   Ricky Martin   Elvis Presley   Elton John

Sting   Bob Dylan   Paul Simon

_____

8. Topic: _____

scanner   copier   CD-ROM   zip drive   printer   monitor   speakers

_____

9. Topic: _____

tide   waves   sand   shells   rocks   picnic   seaweed

_____

10. Topic: _____

canoe   rowboat   kayak   sailboat   parasail   speedboat

_____

Unit 5:   **Topics of Paragraphs**

❖ **Stating the topic of a paragraph**

Test 1

➤   *Write the topic for each paragraph. Be sure your topics are not too general or too specific.*

Seashells

1.   Seashells serve many purposes for the animals that make them. These animals, called mollusks, have soft, squishy bodies with no bones. The shells they make are very hard, and serve as a protection from other animals. Though a few kinds of fish and birds can open or break the shells and eat the mollusks, most cannot. The hard shell also protects the mollusk from being smashed by the waves against rocks on the shore. On the beach, the shell serves yet another purpose: It keeps the mollusk inside from drying out when the tide is low and they are out of the water.

Topic: _____

2.   There are basically two kinds of mollusks that make shells: bivalves and uni-valves. Bivalves have two shells that are joined together. Many of the mollusks that are most commonly used in European or American cooking are bivalves. The bivalves have a kind of "foot" that they can use for digging or moving, but they usually move by quickly opening and closing the two shells. The univalves include many of the mollusks that make the more colorful and spectacular shells that can be found in warm tropical waters. These animals also have a "foot," which allows them to slide along the ocean bottom. Both bivalve and univalve mollusks can close up their shells completely when in danger.

Topic: _____

3.   A seashell collection can be beautiful to look at. It may also be a pleasant re-minder of a happy seaside vacation. Before you start to collect shells, however, you should know a few facts. In some countries or along some beaches, seashells and other forms of coast life are protected, and you are not allowed to take anything from the beach. There may be very strict laws about this. If you take shells from these places and the police discover them, you may have to pay a large fine. In other places, you are allowed to take empty shells. You should put back, however, any shells that still have live mollusks inside them. You would not want to keep them anyway, since they smell terrible when the mollusk dies.

Topic: _____

Unit 5: **Topics of Paragraphs**

❖ **Stating the topic of a paragraph**

Test 2

➤ *Write the topic for each paragraph. Be sure your topics are not too general or too specific.*

Teresa Weatherspoon

1.   Teresa Weatherspoon is the star player on the New York Liberty team in the Women's National Basketball Association. When she comes out at the beginning of a game in New York, her fans go wild. She has many fans—about 13,000 people go to each game she plays in New York. About two million more people watch the games on television. Her team jersey—number 11—is one of the top best-sellers among both men and women players at the National Basketball Association store in New York. People love Teresa because she's a very quick, skillful, and exciting player. Sports writers say that she has the same brilliant playing style as Magic Johnson and other great players. Her New York fans also love her dramatic personality and the energy and enthusiasm with which she leads her team. She seems just right for New York City.

Topic: _____

2.   Teresa Weatherspoon was born in 1965 in a small town in Texas. The youngest of six children, she started playing basketball with her two brothers and their friends. Her father was afraid that she would get hurt, since she was usually the only girl, but she was just as rough and tough as the boys. In high school, Teresa was the star of the girls' basketball team. Then she attended Louisiana Tech, where she led the team to win the college championships. She also led the U.S. women's Olympic basketball team to a gold medal. When she finished college, she knew what she wanted to do—play professional basketball. There were no professional women's teams in the United States at that time, however, so she played for two years in Russia and six years in Italy. Then, in 1996, she returned to the United States to join the Liberty team in New York.

Topic: _____

3.   For many people, Teresa Weatherspoon is not just the star of the Liberty basketball team, she is also a symbol of some recent changes in the world of sports. Girls and women now play competitive sports in school and college. In this way, they learn the skills necessary for playing on a professional level. In fact, women now compete on professional teams in basketball, soccer, and other sports that used to be for men only. Another interesting change has taken place among the sports-watching public. Many more women and girls have become sports fans. Of the 13,000 or more people who go to the Liberty games, about 70 percent are female. For these young girls or women, Teresa Weatherspoon and her teammates are examples of the exciting possibilities for women in sports today.

Topic: _____

Unit 5: **Topics of Paragraphs**
❖ **Stating the topic of a paragraph**

Test 3

➤   *Write the topic for each paragraph. Be sure your topics are not too general or too specific.*

Families

1.   These days, parents talk less with their children than they used to. A recent European study measured the time parents spent in serious conversation with their children. Serious conversation refers to talking about opinions or feelings that are important to someone in the family. The study reports that parents and children in the 1930s spent an average of 25 minutes per day in such conversation. By the 1960s, it was 20 minutes. Today, it is only 8 minutes per day. There are a number of reasons for this change. People generally have less unplanned time for one thing. Also, mealtime and evening conversations are often replaced by watching television. Now with the Internet, family members are spending more time on-line and less time communicating in person.

Topic: _____

2.   Until very recently, babysitters were almost always women. Now, however, taking care of children is no longer considered a job only for women. People are realizing that men can take care of children, too, and in some cases, they may be able to do it better. Many families think it is good for their children to spend time with a man, especially if the children are boys. Some single mothers also feel that a man as a babysitter can help children deal with the lack of a father. Other mothers believe that young men are better as babysitters than women because they are more willing to play games and sports. The children may have more fun with a man, and have more opportunity to get exercise.

Topic: _____

3.   In the United States, if you are a parent and you do not like the schools in your town, you can educate your children at home. This is called homeschooling. There are some guidelines about what children need to learn, and they must be able to pass standardized tests, but the parents are free to teach their children as they want. This freedom is probably why many parents decide on homeschooling. They believe that they can teach their children better than regular schoolteachers can, because they may disagree with the teachers' methods or with the teachers' way of treating the children. These parents are not like most parents. First of all, they have strong ideas about schooling. Furthermore, they have a lot of time at home every day with their children. Homeschooling is not usually possible in families where both parents work.

Topic: _____

Unit 5: **Topics of Paragraphs**

❖ Finding the topic sentence

Test 1

➤ *Each of the paragraphs below is missing the topic sentence. The topic sentences are all listed at the end of the test (with an extra sentence). Read the paragraphs. Choose the best topic sentence for each paragraph. Write the letter of that sentence in the blank.*

Facts about Puerto Rico

1. _____ Puerto Rico is an island found between the Caribbean Sea and the North Atlantic Ocean, about 1,600 kilometers (1,000 miles) southeast of Florida. It is one of the Greater Antilles Islands, a chain that also includes Cuba, Jamaica, and Hispaniola. The island of Puerto Rico covers 9,104 square kilometers (3,525 square miles)—about three times the size of the state of Rhode Island. On it you can find many small rivers, high central mountains, and a large rain forest. Near the 500-mile coast are many large, sunny, and well-watered flat areas ideal for farming. Because of the island's location, it is important for ships on the way to the Panama Canal. Puerto Rico's capital, San Juan, has one of the largest and best harbors in the Caribbean.

2. _____ In addition to its 50 states, the United States has control of 14 small territories, including Puerto Rico, which is called a "commonwealth." This means that the people of Puerto Rico have U.S. citizenship, but only some of the rights of citizens. They are not allowed to vote in presidential elections, and they do not have to pay federal income taxes. However, they carry United States passports, and they may enter and leave the 50 states freely. In fact, over two million Puerto Ricans live in the United States, mostly in the Northeast.

3. When the United States took control of the island of Puerto Rico in 1898, the people there spoke Spanish. In spite of this, the U.S. government insisted that the official language had to be English. Just a few years later, however, a law was passed making both English and Spanish official languages. The public schools were still required to teach only in English, though. This situation continued until 1930, when the Puerto Rican people insisted that schools go back to Spanish, with English taught as a second language. In 1991, Puerto Rican leaders passed a law making Spanish the only official language. In 1993, that law was overturned, and today there are two official languages again. _____

4.   The original residents of Puerto Rico were Taino Indians, and when the Spanish came to the island in the late 1400s, they forced them into slavery. Most of the Taino Indians died from disease or the terrible conditions they worked in. The few remaining Indians married poor Spanish farmers. _____ In the eighteenth and nineteenth centuries, Africans were brought to the island as slaves to work on the big farms. Many Spanish people came from South America, following wars and revolutions in their countries, and French families came from Haiti and Louisiana. Workers in search of a better life also arrived with their families from distant countries, including China, Scotland, Ireland, and even Lebanon. The most recent arrivals to Puerto Rico have come from Cuba and the Dominican Republic.

Missing topic sentences

a. Today's Puerto Rico is a mixture of many races and cultures.

b. Since 1898, Puerto Rico has been part of the United States.

c. It is clear that language has been a big issue in Puerto Rico for many years.

d. In 1898, most people in Puerto Rico worked almost entirely in farming, but today they mostly work in industries located near the big cities.

e. While many people have heard of Puerto Rico, they may not know much about its location and geography.

Unit 5: **Topics of Paragraphs**

❖ **Finding the topic sentence**

Test 2

➤ *Each of the paragraphs below is missing the topic sentence. The topic sentences are all listed at the end of the test (with an extra sentence). Read the paragraphs. Choose the best topic sentence for each paragraph. Write the letter of that sentence in the blank.*

Charles Darwin's Theory

1. Charles Darwin, a recent college graduate and only 23 years old, joined an English scientific expedition in 1832 and sailed to South America on HMS *Beagle*. _____ Throughout the journey, he collected, examined, and made notes about all the living things he saw every time the ship stopped at islands, near mountain ranges, and along rivers. Working with great enthusiasm, he filled many notebooks with careful notes about his observations.

2. _____ This group of islands is located about 600 miles west of Ecuador. Each of the islands is also quite distant from the others, so that animals did not travel easily from one to another or to South America. Darwin noticed that these islands were home to several species of finches (small songbirds). All the finches were very similar, but on each island there were slight differences, especially in the shape of the beak. This shape seemed to be related to the kinds of food available in each place. Darwin wondered why this was so.

3. _____ He was interested, above all, in the question of why species develop differently in different places, and how plants and animals could change or evolve over time. Darwin also read the work of other scientists and thinkers, including philosophers and economists. All of his studies and thinking resulted in the writing of his most famous book, *On the Origin of Species by Means of Natural Selection*.

4. Darwin's book has been called, "the book that shook the world." _____ At that time Darwin's ideas went against those of most other scientists, and some of them argued that he could not prove his theories. The strongest attacks on Darwin, however, were not scientific, but religious. These critics, both in his time and even today, have felt that his ideas go against their belief in God as creator of the world. They have also refused to accept Darwin's view of humans that placed them in the same category as other animals.

Missing topic sentences

a. In fact, from the day it was published in 1859 it has been the cause of fierce intellectual, religious, and political debate.

b. The theories of Thomas Malthus about human populations influenced Darwin's thinking.

c. One place that particularly interested Darwin was the Galapagos Islands.

d. When he returned to England, Darwin worked for years to make sense of all the information he had collected.

e. Though not a naturalist by training, his job on the ship was to make and record information about the plants and animals they found on their travels.

Unit 5: Topics of Paragraphs

❖ Finding the topic sentence

Test 3

➤ *Each of the paragraphs below is missing the topic sentence. The topic sentences are all listed at the end of the test (with an extra sentence). Read the paragraphs. Choose the best topic sentence for each paragraph. Write the letter of that sentence in the blank.*

Animal Communication

1.   When we think about whales, we usually "think big," since whales are the largest animals on Earth. _____ Scientists have seen evidence of this intelligence in the behavior of whales in captivity. First of all, whales have shown that they like to play and that they will care for and help one another, characteristics of the more intelligent animals. Second, there is evidence that in the open ocean whales learn from situations and change their behavior. In captivity, they can be taught by people to do things. Finally, the intelligence of whales is demonstrated by their well-developed system of communication. The humpback whale, for example, makes a low sound. The pilot whale's call, on the other hand, is much higher; it sounds almost like a bird's call.

2.   Research has shown that whales and elephants probably evolved from the same ancestors more than 60 million years ago. _____ People have always known about the sounds elephants make when they are angry or afraid. Now scientists have discovered other sounds that elephants make with their trunks. These sounds are so low that humans cannot normally hear them. Elephants, however, can hear them, and scientists say they sound like the low rumbling of thunder. These low sounds travel far and make it possible for the elephants to communicate over long distances.

3.   _____ Dolphins constantly make two different kinds of sounds. The first is a clicking sound that they use to find food underwater. This system is similar to the system used by bats in the air. The sounds bounce off objects and return to the dolphin with information about what is there. The second kind of sound is a high whistle. Dolphins use this sound in various ways to communicate with other dolphins. Some researchers have trained dolphins to make sounds similar to human words. These researchers believe it may be possible to teach dolphins to communicate with humans in human language.

4.   Unlike whales, elephants, or dolphins, the chimpanzee is a close relative of humans. In fact, the proteins in the human body are almost the same as those in the chimpanzee's body—99 percent the same. Like humans, chimpanzees have a highly developed ability to solve problems. _____ Researchers in the United States have demonstrated the chimpanzee's language ability in several ways. For example, they showed that two chimpanzees named Sherman and Austin actually understood what spoken words represent. They also showed that a chimpanzee named Kanzi could understand more than 150 words when spoken or produced by an electronic speech synthesizer.

Missing topic sentences

a. Vocal communication is also a characteristic of another relative of the whale: the dolphin.

b. Scientists believe this ability may be the reason why chimpanzees are so good at learning human language.

c. These giant creatures may also be among the most intelligent animals on Earth.

d. The communication systems of humans are far more complex than those systems of other animals.

e. Elephants, like whales, are very intelligent and have a system of vocal communication.

Unit 6: **Main Ideas**
❖ **Stating the main idea**

Test 1

➤ *Read each paragraph. Write the topic and a main idea statement. Remember that the main idea must be a complete sentence.*

Wolves

1. What would you do if you saw a wolf in the woods? Would you be afraid? You probably would. As children, most of us heard stories about the big bad wolf. In many of these stories, the wolf kills and eats people. This tradition of stories about the terrible wolf is one reason why there are very few wolves left in North America. Over the past century, as people moved into the western states of the United States, they killed off most of the wolves. In large areas of Alaska and Canada, wolves were also hunted from airplanes for sport. The hunters shot wolves from the air and left them dead. There were even competitions to see who could kill the most wolves. Almost everyone, including the U.S. government, thought that killing the wolves was a good idea.

    Topic: _____

    Main Idea: _____

2. Until quite recently, most Americans knew very little about wolves. The people who did know something about them were the Native Americans. They knew, for example, that wolves rarely kill people. Wolves will only attack if they feel they are in danger. Some Americans, especially hunters, believed that wolves killed many deer and other large animals, so that there were fewer left for the hunters. Native Americans knew that this belief, too, was not true. Wolves only kill other animals when they need food. Even then, they usually kill old or weak animals that will soon die anyway. Finally, the Native Americans knew a lot about the lives and habits of wolves. They knew that in some ways wolves were a lot like humans. In fact, wolves live in family groups and help each other hunt for food and take care of their young.

    Topic: _____

    Main Idea: _____

3.   In the 1960s, Americans began to change their thinking about wolves. This change came about partly because of a general change in attitude about nature and wild animals. People began to see the results of unlimited killing. Many kinds of animals had disappeared or were close to disappearing forever. It was also in part because some scientists began to study the lives of wolves. One of these scientists was a Canadian named Farley Mowat. He lived with wolves in a distant part of northern Canada and wrote a book about what he had learned. This book, *Never Cry Wolf,* was also made into a movie, and through it many people learned to see wolves in a different light. They began to think that wolves were not so terrible, and that the killing of wolves should be stopped.

Topic: _____

Main Idea: _____

Unit 6: Main Ideas

❖ Stating the main idea

Test 2

➤ *Read each paragraph. Write the topic and a main idea statement. Remember that the main idea must be a complete sentence.*

Insects

1. In the historic French Quarter of New Orleans, termites are destroying the buildings. Termites, which are insects that eat wood, have long been a problem in old wooden houses. Now, however, a new kind of termite has arrived from Asia. It is much more destructive than any other kind, and it is causing $300 million of damage every year in New Orleans alone. These Formosan termites can go through paved roads, plastic, and even some kinds of metal to get to wood. Though they arrived in the United States only recently, they have already caused serious damage. They are able to do such serious damage because they multiply fast, especially in hot and humid places like New Orleans. The city is trying to fight these termites, but it is not an easy job. While trying to clean out one old library, for example, workers found 60 to 70 million termites!

    Topic: _____

    Main Idea: _____

2. In the eastern part of the United States, a walk in the woods can be dangerous these days. The danger is from an insect called a deer tick. This small black insect, about the size of the head of a pin, usually lives on deer. It can also attach itself to other animals and to people, however. The problem with a deer tick is not its bite, which you may not even feel. The problem is that when they bite, they can give you Lyme disease. This disease is not too serious if it is discovered early and the right medicines are taken. Many people do not realize, however, that they have been bitten by a deer tick. Doctors also do not always recognize Lyme disease. When the disease is not recognized or treated quickly, it can have permanent effects on your health. The best medicine, doctors say, is prevention. When you go on a walk in the woods, cover your skin. Wear socks, long pants, and long sleeves. Then the deer ticks cannot bite you.

    Topic: _____

    Main Idea: _____

3. We often think of insects as our enemies, and we try to keep them as far away as possible. The screens on our windows keep out some insects. We use sprays and poisons to keep others out. We also think that by washing ourselves we'll have insect-free bodies, too. No amount of hot water and soap can keep mites off us, though. These tiny insects are so small you cannot see them with the human eye, and no human is without them. Some areas of the body, like knees or shoulders, may have few mites. In other areas, especially the face, there may be millions of them. You may not like the idea of insects crawling all over you, but there is no need to worry about these mites. They are completely harmless, and you cannot feel them anyway. In fact, some scientists think that mites may help clean our skin, though how they could do that is still a mystery.

Topic: _____

Main Idea: _____

Unit 6: **Main Ideas**

❖ **Stating the main idea**

Test 3

➤ *Read each paragraph. Write the topic and a main idea statement. Remember that the main idea must be a complete sentence.*

Coffee

1. Some people wonder whether or not they should drink coffee. In fact, for a while some doctors thought that the caffeine in coffee might be bad for the heart. Other doctors thought there might be some danger of cancer from coffee. Now doctors generally agree that coffee is not bad for you at all, if you do not drink too much of it. While drinking too much coffee could increase your risk of heart disease, drinking no more than three or four cups a day seems to have no permanent negative effects. There may even be a small positive effect on our blood and heart, according to the recent Scottish Health Study. Coffee also has a positive effect on your ability to think. After a cup of coffee, your brain works faster and better.

Topic: _____

Main Idea: _____

2. In many European countries in the eighteenth and nineteenth centuries, a café was an important gathering place. People went there to read the newspaper, to discuss politics and art, to meet friends, or just to have a good cup of coffee. For much of the twentieth century, people had less time and interest in sitting and talking. They also seemed to lose interest in good coffee. As a result, the café lost its importance as a meeting place. Toward the end of the twentieth century, however, it began to come back into fashion, so now there are many cafés in most cities. Some of the classic old cafés are popular once again, and there are also many new cafés. Some, like Starbucks or Peets, are part of American chains of cafés that all look alike and sell the same kind of coffee. Other cafés are designed in different styles, from ultramodern to old-fashioned. Some can be found along main streets, and others are located in bookstores and department stores. Whatever their style or location, they all offer you a chance to sit down, relax, and enjoy a cup of coffee.

Topic: _____

Main Idea: _____

3.   If you wanted to open a café in your city, where would you go for ideas? Italy, of course. There are more cafés there than in any other country—one for every 400 people. More specifically, you should go to Naples. This city is famous for its excellent and very strong coffee. It is also home to a new "Coffee University," where you can learn all you ever need to know about coffee. There are lessons on the history and production of coffee and on the business of running a café. There are also lessons about another side to café management: the quality of the service. In Naples, you are taught that running a successful café is a kind of art. The place has to have a good feeling about it, so that people want to go there. This depends partly on the speed and quality of the service. It also depends a great deal on how the waiters relate to the customers.

Topic: _____

Main Idea: _____

Unit 7: **Patterns of Organization**

❖ **Recognizing patterns in sentences**

Test 1

➤ *Each of the sentences below is a possible beginning for a newspaper article. Decide which pattern you think the writer will use in the article. Then write the letters of that pattern beside the sentence.*

L—Listing   S—Sequence   CC—Comparison/Contrast   CE—Cause/Effect

_____   1. The lives of Vincent St. James, a 56-year-old delivery man, and Redmond Oliver, a homeless 51-year-old, became connected three years ago when Mr. St. James gave Mr. Oliver 50 cents for a cup of coffee.

_____   2. A tiny computer chip makes it possible to build hand-held computers.

_____   3. Scientists at Brown University said yesterday that they have found many reasons to believe that Mars once had a wide ocean with waves and beaches.

_____   4. When astronauts arrived on the new space station, they found many new and improved instruments that were not on the *Mir,* the abandoned Russian station.

_____   5. Nelson Mandela, former president of South Africa, will visit Florida after his meeting with Bill Gates in Seattle.

_____   6. Japanese space engineers announced that they would not continue the H-2 rocket project after a series of costly failures.

_____   7. Like the Internet today, the transcontinental railroad across the United States, completed in 1869, connected the American people across the country.

_____   8. Although he knows the importance of his work in helping the homeless in Milwaukee, Wisconsin, many of Michael King's daily experiences discourage him.

_____   9. The president and the executives of many U.S. technology companies will begin next week to carry out their plan to make computers and the Internet as common as the telephone.

_____   10. The space shuttle *Discovery* is going to be delayed until late next week so workers can replace a dented fuel line, NASA reported today.

Unit 7: **Patterns of Organization**

❖ **Recognizing patterns in sentences**

Test 2

➤ *Each of the sentences below is a possible beginning for a newspaper article. Decide which pattern you think the writer will use in the article. Then write the letters of that pattern beside the sentence.*

L—Listing   S—Sequence   CC—Comparison/Contrast   CE—Cause/Effect

_____   1. While the fans seemed to love the older skaters, the youngest athletes performed the best in the world professional figure skating championship held in Washington last week.

_____   2. The French government refused to approve the sale of British beef in France, so the European Commission said it would begin legal action against the French.

_____   3. Oscar Kissin, whose concert last night was a great success in Carnegie Hall, has much to celebrate this Thanksgiving.

_____   4. At the beginning of the 1900s, a Missouri farmer invented a machine for making smooth roads.

_____   5. While some people think that buying products over the Internet, or e-commerce, is a totally new way of shopping, it is actually not much different from ordering products from a catalog over the phone.

_____   6. The Sears Roebuck Company catalog, which was first printed in 1915, was more than 1,000 pages long and included tens of thousands of items in 24 departments.

_____   7. Like catalog shopping, the new e-commerce has resulted in an increase in the number of companies that ship people's orders to their homes by truck, plane, and ship.

_____   8. Melinda Donato, a 15-year-old champion athlete from Miami High School, began running races at the age of six and has been winning championships since she was ten.

_____   9. Swedish women swimmers broke three major world records yesterday at the European Swimming Championships in Lisbon, Portugal.

_____ 10. A traveler to Vietnam's major cities today will find many dramatic changes.

Unit 7: **Patterns of Organization**

❖ **Recognizing patterns in short passages**

Test 1

➤ *In each paragraph, there is a different pattern and a missing sentence. Decide what the pattern is and which sentence fits best. The missing sentences (plus one extra) are listed at the end of the test. Then decide what the overall pattern of the whole passage is.*

L—Listing   S—Sequence   CC—Comparison/Contrast   CE—Cause/Effect

Women in American Sports

1.   One hundred years ago, American women were not very active in sports. Most women did not take part in athletic activities at all because people thought only men should play sports. Many sports, especially team sports, were considered too difficult or violent for women. They could only play tennis or golf, or go skiing, ice-skating, or swimming. Even in these sports, very few women took part in competitions, and even fewer played professionally. This situation remained unchanged until after the first half of the twentieth century. _____ Some women wanted to be able to play more sports, and so they tried to get more opportunities. It took some years, however, before their efforts brought any results. As late as 1970, only one in 27 high school girls was involved in athletic activities.

Sentence: _____   Pattern: _____

2.   Real change in women's sports came after 1972, with a new law called Title IX (Title Nine). This law made a dramatic change in how schools and colleges spent government money on sports. Before Title IX, they had spent the government money mostly on boys' and men's sports. Part of the reason for this was financial. The boys' and men's teams often earned money for the schools and colleges through sales of tickets to games. After Title IX, however, schools and colleges had to spend the same amount of money on women's and girls' sports as on men's and boys'. _____ They also had to buy new equipment and hire new teachers and trainers for the women students.

Sentence: _____   Pattern: _____

3.   At first, no one was sure what effect Title IX would have in the long term. Those people who were against the law worried about financial issues. They thought that schools and colleges would lose money because of the law. They also thought that girls and women would not really be interested in sports. They were sure that all the new rooms and equipment would not be used. It soon became clear, however, that this was not true. As schools and colleges began to spend more money on girls' and women's sports, interest in the sports grew. Girls and women began to play baseball, basketball, soccer, rugby, hockey, and other competitive team sports. They also began to compete in running, rowing, cycling, and other kinds of races. _____

Sentence: _____   Pattern: _____

4.   Now, almost 30 years after Title IX was passed, women's sports have become enormously popular. This fact is demonstrated by the number of high school girls who were involved in sports in 1999: one in three. _____ Equipment and shoes for women's sports now have multi-million dollar sales. Big companies are paying women athletes, such as the tennis player Mary Pierce, to design products for them. Women now play professionally in many sports that were once for men only. In basketball, for instance, the games played by the teams of the Women's National Basketball Association—started in 1996—attract large crowds at the stadiums and large audiences on television. Women have also been successful in soccer. When the U.S. women's soccer team played the final game of the 1999 Women's World Cup tournament, 90,000 fans watched them win the championship.

Sentence: _____   Pattern: _____

Missing sentences

a. Another sign of the popularity of women's sports is in the business world.

b. The tennis player, Billie Jean King, did much to promote women in tennis in America.

c. Then, in the 1960s, people began to change their ideas about women in American society.

d. Because of this growing participation, women's athletic performances improved greatly and records were broken.

e. Under the new law, college sports departments had to build new showers and dressing rooms for women.

What is the overall pattern of the whole passage? _____

Unit 7: **Patterns of Organization**
❖ **Recognizing patterns in short passages**

Test 2

➤ *In each paragraph, there is a different pattern and a missing sentence. Decide what the pattern is and which sentence fits best. The missing sentences (plus one extra) are listed at the end of the test. Then decide what the overall pattern of the whole passage is.*

L—Listing   S—Sequence   CC—Comparison/Contrast   CE—Cause/Effect

The American Civil War

1.   In 1860, the United States was in danger of breaking up into two countries. Six southern states decided at the end of that year to leave the government of the United States—the Union—and form their own government—the Confederacy. President Abraham Lincoln and the Union government did not want a war. _____ The Confederate government wanted complete independence, however, especially from the Union military. By the spring of 1861, all the Union soldiers had left the South except for a small group of soldiers in South Carolina. President Lincoln decided that these soldiers should stay. When Confederate soldiers attacked these Union soldiers on April 12 of that year, Lincoln finally had to declare war.

Sentence: _____   Pattern: _____

2.   The four years of civil war that followed brought death and hardship to many Americans, both northern and southern. Americans were fighting Americans on land and at sea. Families were torn apart, with some relatives fighting for the Confederacy and others for the Union. Disease spread through both armies. More soldiers died from malaria, typhoid, and dysentery than from the fighting. Over 620,000 people died in the Civil War—more than in all the other wars in which the United States has fought. _____ In the South, especially, cities were destroyed and many people lost their homes.

Sentence: _____   Pattern: _____

3.   At the time of the Civil War, the armies were made up of volunteers—people who wanted to fight. Among these volunteers, many women worked hard to help their side win the war. _____ More than 400 women dressed as men and went into battle alongside the other soldiers. Still other women became spies. They would go into inns and cafes and try to get information and military secrets from the soldiers. For all these women, the conditions were very difficult and often dangerous. Many women, like the men, died from disease.

Sentence: _____   Pattern: _____

4.   The Civil War finally came to an end on April 9, 1865, in Appomatox, Virginia. The commander of the Confederate army, General Robert E. Lee, surrendered to General Ulysses S. Grant, the commander of the Union army. These two leaders have often been compared. Although they were on opposite sides during the war, they were similar in several ways. Both were great commanders who knew how to lead armies. _____ Grant and Lee also both had strong, quick minds and the ability to understand a situation quickly. Both, at the end of the war, had the ability to turn quickly from war to peace. The way they behaved at Appomatox helped to bring peace to the United States.

Sentence: _____   Pattern: _____

Missing sentences

a. Some women went to the army camps to cook meals and wash the soldiers' clothes.

b. In the early part of 1861, Lincoln tried to find a way to avoid fighting.

c. General Grant showed his greatness as a leader of the Union army in Tennessee.

d. Their style of fighting was very much alike, and so was their refusal to give up.

e. The war also caused great destruction.

What is the overall pattern of the whole passage? _____

Unit 7: Patterns of Organization

❖ Recognizing patterns in short passages

Test 3

➤ *In each paragraph, there is a different pattern and a missing sentence. Decide what the pattern is and which sentence fits best. The missing sentences (plus one extra) are listed at the end of the test. Then decide what the overall pattern of the whole passage is.*

L—Listing   S—Sequence   CC—Comparison/Contrast   CE—Cause/Effect

The History of Reading and Books

1.   The earliest "books" were made in Western Asia beginning in about 3000 BC. They were not made of paper, however. They were large, rectangular pieces of clay, wax, or stone called "tablets." Words were carved onto the heavy tablets using a stylus—a sharp, pointed tool. _____ They wrote on long strips of papyrus by hand and then rolled up the strips onto big sticks. This form of book is called a scroll. Scrolls were not as heavy as tablets, but they were large and very difficult to hold. In about the third or fourth century AD, people began cutting the long strips of scrolls into smaller pieces. These pieces were sewn together in the middle, and this new invention was called a "codex."

Sentence: _____   Pattern: _____

2.   The development of the codex was very important for several reasons. First of all, it was light and easy to hold. With the two pages side by side, it was easier to read the text. It was also possible to read faster, since turning pages was quicker than unrolling scrolls. In addition, the people who read a codex often wrote page numbers in it. That made it even easier to look for information quickly. _____ That meant that more people had a chance to see a codex, and so more people became interested in learning to read.

Sentence: _____   Pattern: _____

3.   The form of a text affects how it is read. The early "books"—tablet, scroll, or codex—were written with no spaces between the words and no punctuation. _____ Because of the difficulty of reading these early texts, very few people learned to read at all. Most people depended on the few readers they knew to read aloud to them. Thus, reading was not an individual activity, as it usually is today, but a group experience. By the time the printing press was invented in the fifteenth century, this had begun to change. Words were printed separately and sentences were punctuated to make reading easier. The printing press made it possible to produce great numbers of books, so many more people could own books and more people could learn to read.

Sentence: _____   Pattern: _____

4.   The newest form of book is the so-called "e-book." Instead of keeping books on shelves at home or in a library, you can store and read them on a small, hand-held computer the size of a paperback book. Instead of stopping to find a new word in a traditional dictionary, you can find the definition in the computer's built-in dictionary with a click of the mouse. Though the form may seem different, reading on a computer screen is similar to reading a regular paper book in several important ways. _____ It has margins, just like a book page, and the print used in e-books is the same style that is found in regular paper books. Readers can even write in the margins of the e-book and save their place with an e-bookmark.

Sentence: _____   Pattern: _____

Missing sentences

a. Some people still like to listen to someone reading aloud.

b. First, the screen looks like a book page.

c. In one of these texts, *thewordswouldlooklikethis*

d. Then, in about 2800 BC, Egyptians discovered how to make papyrus, a paper-like material.

e. Furthermore, it was small enough to carry around.

What is the overall pattern of the whole passage? _____

Unit 8: **Skimming**

Test 1

➤ *Skim the selections about chimpanzees from two different encyclopedias. Read the questions and then skim both entries to find the answers. Time limit: 7 minutes.*

1. Which selection is shorter, A or B? _____

2. In which selection is there more information about pygmy chimpanzees? _____

3. In which selection can you find information about chimpanzees learning to speak? _____

4. What are some examples of chimpanzee intelligence? _____
   _____

5. In which selection can you find information about the similarities between chimpanzees and human beings? _____

6. What is one example of the similarity between chimpanzees and humans? _____
   _____

7. What is one book that both selections suggest for further reading? _____
   _____

8. Which selection has more specific details about what chimpanzees eat? _____

9. In which selection can you find more detailed information about how long chimpanzees usually live? _____

10. In which selection can you find more detailed information about newborn chimpanzees? _____

Selection A

CHIMPANZEE, chim-pan-'zē, a great ape native to the dense forests and open woodlands of west and central equatorial Africa. The common chimpanzee is classified as a single species, *Pan troglodytes,* but there is as much variation among chimpanzees as among men. The pigmy chimpanzee is considered by many authorities to be a distinct species, *Pan paniscus.* Chimpanzees are highly intelligent social animals closely related to man, and for this reason they are valuable for use in medical and behavioral research.

Characteristics. Adult chimpanzees have few natural enemies other than disease, for they are large, powerfully built animals that stand about 4.5 feet (1.3 meters) high and weigh an average of 115 pounds (52 kg). There are wide individual differences, and the male tends to be somewhat larger and more robust than the female.

The gestation period of the chimpanzee is 7 months, and the newborn animal weighs about 4 pounds (1.8 kg). It is almost as helpless as a human infant. It clutches the hair on its mother's sides and back while it clings to her chest and stomach. Only the head has any appreciable amount of black hair at birth; there is a white tuft at the anal region, and another is often found at the chin. The hair tends to lighten with age, whereas the skin darkens. Some individuals develop black faces early in life, but others only develop a tan face color.

As the infant chimpanzee grows, it begins to explore the world; it starts to ride on the mother's back when she travels. A new infant is seldom born before the last one is two or three years old. Even at that age the juvenile chimpanzee remains closely associated with its mother, although it spends more and more time with its playmates and other members of its band. The chimpanzee reaches full stature at about age 12; few achieve the potential life-span of over 50.

Behavior. A band of chimpanzees, which usually contains 6 to 10 members, exists as part of a larger community of bands. These bands may exchange members, merge, or divide, depending on available foods and other factors. Some bands consist only of adult males or of mothers and young, but individuals appear to come and go freely within the community.

Much of the life of the chimpanzees is spent in the trees, where they sleep and obtain the fruits that constitute the bulk of their diet. They also eat other vegetable matter and insects, and there are reliable reports of chimpanzees killing and eating small mammals. The apes seldom venture far from trees, and they avoid direct sunlight. A sleeping nest is built each night, and a resting platform may be built during the day.

The chimpanzee's long arms are suited to brachiation (swinging through trees), but most purposeful travel takes place on the ground. Chimpanzees walk on the soles of the feet and the middle phalanges of the flexed fingers. A chimpanzee can also stand erect on its short stocky legs. Some individuals may travel short distances on their legs only, especially when the hands are being used to carry an object. When excited, males often stand on their legs and also put on an impressive display. The display usually starts with swaying or stamping and with vocal sounds that reach a crescendo scream. This may be followed either with a final charge or the flinging of objects, or both. These displays, however, seldom express directed aggression.

Chimpanzees do not swim. Therefore the major rivers in the rain forests where they live may be effective barriers separating the different races of chimpanzees.

Intelligence. Chimpanzees are very responsive and easily excited animals, and they enter into many tasks with great exuberance. They display great versatility in the range of problems they can solve and in their ability to manipulate objects and fashion crude tools. Although their performances on particular tasks may be matched by some monkeys, no monkey tested has been able to equal the versatility of the chimpanzee.

Young chimpanzees often become strongly attached to their trainers, and even adult chimpanzees show partiality to certain people. The chimpanzee is, above all, an intelligent social animal requiring companionship and a sufficiently stimulating environment to keep it active and interested in life.

Chimpanzees are classified in the family Pongidae, suborder Anthropoidea, order Primates.

IRWIN S. BERNSTEIN
Yerkes Regional Primate Center
Emory University

Further reading: Ghiglieri, M., *East of the Mountains of the Moon* (Free Press, 1987); Goodall, Jane, *The Chimpanzees of Gombe* (Harvard University Press, 1986).

Chimpanzee is an African ape. Chimpanzees are one of the four kinds of apes, along with gibbons, gorillas, and orang-utans. The chimpanzee ranks as one of the most intelligent animals and resembles human beings more closely than any other animal.

Chimpanzees have many characteristics that make them especially interesting and valuable to human beings. The chimpanzee's playfulness and curiosity make it a popular animal at zoos. Young chimpanzees can be tamed and trained easily, and they make excellent circus performers. Scientists use chimpanzees in medical and psychological research because the animals have many similarities to human beings.

Most zoologists classify chimpanzees into two species. The first species is known simply as the chimpanzee. It lives throughout much of central Africa, from Lake Victoria in the east to Sierra Leone in the west. Scientists divide this species into three subspecies—the common, or masked, chimpanzee; the tschego; and the eastern, or long-haired, chimpanzee. The second species, known as the pygmy chimpanzee or bonobo, lives only in Zaire, south of the Congo River and west of the Lualaba River. This article discusses primarily the first species.

The body of a chimpanzee. Chimpanzees range in height from $3^{1}/4$ feet (1 meter) to $5^{1}/2$ feet (1.7 meters). An adult male weighs about 110 pounds (50 kilograms). An adult female weighs about 90 pounds (41 kilograms).

The chimpanzee's body is covered with long, black hair. Like the other apes, the chimpanzee does not have a tail. It has large ears, and its arms are longer than its legs. The chimpanzee's long hands are well adapted for grasping and holding onto objects. In addition, the big toes of the chimpanzee face sideways like thumbs, enabling it to grasp branches with its feet while climbing.

Baldness is common among both male and female chimpanzees. The bald area in males forms a triangle on the forehead. The bald patch in female chimpanzees extends from the forehead to the crown of the head.

The life of a chimpanzee. Chimpanzees live in forests, including tropical rain forests, and in forested, grassy plains. They move about in search of food and usually range over an area of 10 to 20 square miles (26 to 52 square kilometers). Chimpanzees travel in groups that vary in number and change members frequently. There are four chief types of groups: (1) bands of adult males and females, (2) all-male bands, (3) bands of mothers and their infants, and (4) mixed bands of both sexes and all ages. Sometimes a chimpanzee may travel alone.

Chimpanzees live both in trees and on the ground. They spend from 50 to 75 percent of each day in the trees. They sleep in tree nests made of branches, leaves, and twigs. The animals make new nests each night. They build the nests at least 15 feet (4.6 meters) above the ground. When resting during the day, chimpanzees lie along a limb and grasp overhead branches, or they may sprawl out on the ground.

Chimpanzees usually walk on all fours, supporting the upper part of their bodies with their knuckles. They seldom stand erect to walk or run, except when excited or to see over tall grass. The males occasionally show off their strength by walking upright, waving branches, and screaming loudly.

The chimpanzee's chief foods include fruits, leaves, seeds, and stems. They also eat ants, bird eggs, fish, and termites. They occasionally kill and eat baboons, wild hogs called *bush pigs,* and red-tail monkeys.

Chimpanzees in the wild mate chiefly from August to November, but those in captivity mate more frequently throughout the year. Most females bear their first young at the age of 11 or 12 years. The pregnancy period lasts about 230 days. In most cases, the female gives birth to a single baby. Female chimpanzees generally give birth once every three or four years.

The females raise their young almost entirely by themselves. The infants ride under the mother's body, supported by her arm, until they are about 5 months old. Then they ride on the mother's back. Young chimpanzees often chase one another playfully through the trees. They leave their mothers at about 6 years of age.

Chimpanzees seldom fight among themselves or become aggressive. The adults spend about an hour each day in a friendly, social activity called *grooming*. During this period, two or more chimpanzees sit and pick through each other's hair. They remove any dirt, insects, leaves, or burs that they might find.

Chimpanzees express themselves vocally by means of barks, grunts, and screams. When they find a large food supply, the animals jump through the trees, hoot loudly, and beat on tree trunks. This activity alerts all other chimpanzees within hearing distance. They also communicate with body gestures. Chimpanzees may greet each other by touching various parts of the other's body or by embracing. Their facial expressions cover a wide variety of emotions, including excitement, fear, and rage.

Chimpanzees make and use tools more than any other animal except human beings. For example, they strip the leaves from stems and use the stems as tools to catch termites. They also use leaves to make "sponges" for soaking up water to drink.

Biologists believe chimpanzees live from 30 to 38 years in their natural surroundings. They generally live from 40 to 60 years in zoos and research centers.

Pygmy chimpanzees are slightly smaller and lighter than other chimpanzees. Adult male pygmy chimpanzees weigh about 100 pounds (45 kilograms) and adult females weigh about 73 pounds (33 kilograms). Pygmy chimpanzees live only in a small area of rain forest in Zaire. These chimpanzees are very acrobatic. They jump and dive, hang from branches, and walk on two legs more often than other chimpanzees.

Unlike other chimpanzees, pygmy chimpanzees live in permanent groups of males, females, and infants. The groups may consist of from 5 to 30 individuals. Groups frequently gather to share food.

Research on chimpanzees. Chimpanzees and human beings share many physical and social traits. For example, human and chimpanzee polypeptides (compounds that make up proteins) are 99 percent identical. In addition, human beings and chimpanzees both have similar abilities to solve certain problems.

Because of the chimpanzee's many similarities to human beings, scientists frequently use these apes in research. Psychologists use chimpanzees in the study of certain kinds of behavior, such as communication, intelligence, and learning. In one experiment, chimpanzees were shown an object and then given two objects to feel. By feeling, the chimpanzees learned to identify the object that was identical to the one they had seen. Scientists once believed that only human beings had this ability.

Beginning in the 1960's, scientists attempted to teach sign language and other types of language to chimpanzees. Scientists at the University of Nevada in Reno taught more than 160 signs of the American Sign Language to a chimpanzee named Washoe. Washoe learned the names of objects and actions. In the opinion of some researchers, she also combined signs in meaningful ways. During the 1970's and 1980's, many other chimpanzees were taught sign language. At the Yerkes Primate Research Center in Atlanta, Georgia, a chimpanzee named Lana learned to use various symbols on a computer keyboard to ask for food, companionship, and music.

In spite of such accomplishments in teaching chimpanzees to use sign language or symbols, some researchers questioned whether the apes had learned to use language the way people do. These researchers acknowledged that chimpanzees had learned to use "words" (either hand signs or symbols) in appropriate situations. But they doubted that the chimpanzees understood what the signs or symbols represented.

In 1980, researchers at the Yerkes Primate Research Center presented evidence that chimpanzees can understand what symbols really mean. Two chimpanzees, named Sherman and Austin, were shown various symbols. The two apes previously had learned to associate each of these symbols with a certain food or tool. After viewing each symbol, the chimpanzees classified it by pressing a "food" or a "tool" symbol on a keyboard. Sherman and Austin consistently put each symbol into the correct category the first time they were shown it. Their responses indicated that they understood what the symbols represented, much as people understand what words represent.

Later research at Yerkes with a male pygmy chimpanzee named Kanzi has provided further evidence of the ability of chimpanzees to understand language. Kanzi understands more than 150 words produced either by human speech or by electronic speech synthesis. In response to each word, he selects the correct word-symbol on a keyboard and does so without training.

The great demand for chimpanzees for research and other purposes has created a serious threat to the animals. Human beings hunt chimpanzees for export to research institutions, circuses, and zoos. In some areas, people hunt chimpanzees for food and for use as household pets. In addition, people have destroyed many of the forests and grassy plains where the animals once lived. Some African countries have established game preserves in order to protect chimpanzees. Conservationists have also proposed the development of captive breeding programs to stop the threat to wild chimpanzee populations.

Scientific classification. Chimpanzees belong to the anthropoid ape family, Pongi-dae. They make up the genus *Pan.* The scientific name for the chimpanzee is *P. troglodytes,* and the pygmy chimpanzee is *P. paniscus.*

Duane M. Rumbaugh

See also **Ape; Goodall, Jane.**

Additional Resources

Ghiglieri, Michael P. *East of the Mountains of the Moon: Chimpanzee Society in the African Rain Forest.* Free Press, 1988.

Goodall, Jane. *The Chimpanzees of Gombe: Patterns of Behavior.* Belknap, 1986. *The Chimpanzee Family Book.* Picture Bk. Studio, 1991, first published in 1989. For younger readers: *Through a Window: My Thirty Years with the Chimpanzees of Gombe.* Houghton, 1990.

Heltne, Paul G., and Marquardt, L. A., Eds. *Understanding Chimpanzees.* Harvard Univ. Press, 1989.

Savage-Rumbaugh, E. Sue. *Ape Language: From Conditioned Response to Symbol.* Columbia Univ. Press, 1986.

Wall, Frans B. de. *Chimpanzee Politics: Power and Sex Among Apes.* Johns Hopkins, 1989, first published in 1982.

Unit 9:   Making Inferences

❖ Making inferences from short stories

Test 1

➤ *Read this passage from* The Hitchhiker, *a story by Roald Dahl. Try to infer the answers to the questions below. Then underline the words or phrases that helped you.*

The Hitchhiker

"You never saw nothin'," he said proudly. "You never even saw me move an inch. And you know why?"

"Yes," I said. "Because you've got fantastic fingers."

"Exactly right!" he cried. "You catch on pretty quick, don't you?" He sat back and sucked away at his home-made cigarette, blowing the smoke out in a thin stream against the windshield. He knew he had impressed me greatly with those tricks, and this made him very happy. "I don't want to be late," he said. "What time is it?"

"There's a clock in front of you," I told him.

"I don't trust car clocks," he said. "What time does your watch say?"

I hitched up my sleeve to look at the watch on my wrist. It wasn't there. I looked at the man. He looked back at me, grinning.

"You've taken that, too," I said.

He held out his hand and there was my watch lying in his palm. "Nice bit of stuff, this," he said. "Superior quality. Eighteen-carat gold. Easy to flog, too. It's never any trouble gettin' rid of quality goods."

"I'd like it back, if you don't mind," I said rather huffily.

He placed the watch carefully on the leather tray in front of him. "I wouldn't nick anything from you, guv'nor," he said. "You're my pal. You're giving me a lift."

"I'm glad to hear it," I said.

"All I'm doin' is answerin' your questions," he went on. "You asked me what I did for a livin' and I'm showin' you."

"What else have you got of mine?"

He smiled again, and now he started to take from the pocket of his jacket one thing after another that belonged to me—my driving-license, a key-ring with four keys on it, some pound notes, a few coins, a letter from my publisher, my diary, a stubby old pencil, a cigarette-lighter, and last of all, a beautiful old sapphire ring with pearls around it belonging to my wife. I was taking the ring up to the jeweler in London because one of the pearls was missing.

1. Who are the characters in this story? _____

2. Are they men or women? _____

3. Where are they? _____

4. What happened just before this passage in the story? _____

_____

5. What do you think will happen next? _____

_____

Unit 9: **Making Inferences**

❖ **Making inferences from short stories**

Test 2

➤ **Read this passage from Honor Thy Father and Thy Mother, *a story by Judith Chernaik.* Try to infer the answers to the questions below. Then underline the words or phrases that helped you.**

◀ **Honor Thy Father and Thy Mother** ▶

In early fall I applied for admission to college. Where should I go but to fabled Ithaca? [Cornell University] My mother fought bitterly against it, and when she saw me studying a photograph of my father grinning quizzically at the world from the lap of Ezra Cornell, she tore it up angrily.

"You can't say it's not a great university, just because Papa went there."

"That's not it at all." She was still holding the pieces in her hand. "We can't afford to send you away to college, not as things are now."

"I wouldn't dream of asking you for money. Do you want me to get a job to help support you and Papa? Things aren't that bad, are they?"

"No," she said icily. "I do not expect you to contribute to our support."

Father had apprenticed himself for some months to Grandfather Isadore, and was now installed in the small jewelry shop on the Bowery. His chief customers were his old college friends, Herb and Maxie, and his rich cousin Abe. My mother exerted herself to move out

of her cocoon; she picked up a long-lapsed membership in local chapters of Planned Parenthood and the League of Women Voters, so that when Father sent out his new cards, together they were able to draw up a respectable list of names. Whether the names would turn into customers was another question, and I knew that my parents were resigned to a long period of waiting before their modest investment could begin to show returns.

Analyzing my parents' failures, I decided that they had not wanted enough to be rich and successful; otherwise they could not possibly have mismanaged their lives so badly. I was torn between the desire to help them, to change their lives, to present them with some extraordinary gift, and the determination not to repeat their mistakes. I had a superstitious belief in my power to get what I wanted, which events seemed to confirm; after months of dogged studying I won a full college scholarship. My father could barely contain his pride in me, and my mother reluctantly yielded before my triumph and his.

1. Who is the narrator of the story? _____

2. Who are the other members of the family and how does the narrator feel about

   them? _____

3. What is the father's job? _____

4. What can you tell about the past? _____

5. What do you think will happen after this in the story? _____

   _____

Unit 9: Making Inferences

❖ Making inferences from short stories

Test 3

➤ *Read this passage from* The Jilting of Granny Weatherall, *a story by Katherine Anne Porter. ("To jilt" means to leave or reject a lover suddenly.) Try to infer the answers to the questions at the end of the passage. Then underline the words or phrases that helped you.*

The Jilting of Granny Weatherall

She must get up and pull the shades down or she'd never sleep. She was in bed again and the shades were not down. How could that happen? Better turn over, hide from the light, sleeping in that light gave you nightmares. "Mother, how do you feel now?" and a stinging wetness on her forehead. But I don't like having my face washed in cold water!

Hapsy? George? Lydia? Jimmy? No, Cornelia, and her features were swollen and full of little puddles. "They're coming, darling, they'll all be here soon." Go wash your face, child, you look funny.

Instead of obeying, Cornelia knelt down and put her head on the pillow. She seemed to be talking but there was no sound. "Well, are you tongue-tied? Whose birthday is it? Are you going to give a party?"

Cornelia's mouth moved urgently in strange shapes. "Don't do that, you bother me, daughter."

"Oh, no, Mother. Oh, no . . . "

Nonsense. It was strange about children. They disputed your every word. "No what, Cornelia?"

"Here's Doctor Harry."

"I won't see that boy again. He just left five minutes ago."

"That was this morning, Mother. It's night now. Here's the nurse."

"This is Doctor Harry, Mrs. Weatherall. I never saw you look so young and happy!"

"Ah, I'll never be young again—but I'd be happy if they'd let me lie in peace and get rested."

She thought she spoke up loudly, but no one answered. A warm weight on her forehead, a warm bracelet on her wrist, and a breeze went on whispering, trying to tell her something. A shuffle of leaves in the everlasting hand of God, he blew on them and they danced and rattled. "Mother, don't mind, we're going to give you a little hypodermic." "Look here, daughter, how do ants get in this bed? I saw sugar ants yesterday." Did you send for Hapsy too?

It was Hapsy she really wanted. She had to go a long way back through a great many rooms to find Hapsy standing with a baby on her arm. She seemed to herself to be Hapsy also, and the baby on Hapsy's arm was Hapsy and himself and herself, all at once, and there was no surprise in the meeting. Then Hapsy melted from within and turned flimsy as gray gauze and the baby was a gauzy shadow, and Hapsy came up close and said, "I thought you'd never come," and looked at her very searchingly and said, "You haven't changed a bit!" They leaned forward to kiss, when Cornelia began whispering from a long way off, "Oh, is there anything you want to tell me? Is there anything I can do for you?"

Yes, she had changed her mind after sixty years and she would like to see George. I want you to find George. Find him and be sure to tell him I forgot him. I want him to know I had my husband just the same and my children and my house like any other woman. A good house too and a good husband that I loved and fine children out of him. Better than I hoped for even. Tell him I was given back everything he took away and more. Oh, no, oh, God, no, there was something else besides the house and the man and the children. Oh, surely they were not all? What was it? Something not given back . . .

1. Who is the "she" who is narrating this story? _____

2. Where is she? _____

3. Who are the other people mentioned? _____

4. What can you tell about the past? _____

_____

5. What do you think will happen after this in the story? _____

_____

Unit 9: **Making Inferences**

❖ **Inferring topics and main ideas**

Test 1

➤ *In these paragraphs, the topic is never stated directly. Infer what each paragraph is about and write the topic below. Underline any words or phrases that helped you guess.*

1.   When you're very young it seems impossible. You may try, but the results are usually not successful. You may even end up falling and hurting yourself if an adult does not notice a mistake and do it for you again. Then, about the time you start school, it begins to get easier. Still, children often forget and their mothers have to remind them. Sooner or later, though, you stop thinking about it and it becomes completely automatic. There can occasionally be problems, though. You may be in a hurry and do a poor job, or it may be that you are not using the best method. In fact, in different countries people do it different ways, and some of these methods work better than others. In any case, there is nothing more annoying than having to stop and do it again. You could run into trouble, though, if you don't!

    Topic: _____

2.   It means something different to different people. For some people, it tells the world who they are. They are not as interested in how well it works, or how well it serves their needs. The important thing is to choose one that is expensive and fashionable. What they really want is to show the world that they can afford it. For that reason, they generally get a new one every few years, and they try to get the biggest one possible. Other people, however, have a very different point of view. For them, it is simply a necessity. They try to spend as little money as possible, and they want something that will give them as little trouble as possible. In some cases, depending on the family, a large one may be necessary. Otherwise, these people often prefer a small one because it is generally cheaper, less trouble, and easier to use. Furthermore, they like to keep it as long as possible—as long as it still works. They do not mind if it is old and unfashionable.

    Topic: _____

Unit 9: **Making Inferences**

❖ **Inferring topics and main ideas**

Test 2

➤ *Read the book reviews and try to infer the reviewer's opinion of the book. Underline any words or phrases that helped you guess. Then answer the questions.*

1. Over the years since the famous musician Richard Strauss died, a number of biographies have been written about him. Now there is another one written by a well-known journalist. In a biography about a great musician, the reader expects to learn about his background and his life. In this new biography, his life is described in great detail. We learn about every illness, every love affair, every letter he ever sent, and every person he ever met. We learn absolutely nothing new about his music, however. This is a man who inspired a revolution in the way people thought about music in his time, but this biography is limited to a few brief comments about the opinions his wives and lovers had about his music. We are told that he wrote music, but we are not told anything about the music itself or how if affected other musicians. If you are interested only in Richard Strauss as a person, this book will give you a complete picture. If you are interested in the man and his music, read something else!

    a. What is the reviewer's opinion of this book?

    _____

    b. How do you know?

    _____

2. Though this book may be found in the children's section of a bookstore or library, it is not necessarily only for children. A reader of any age will be touched, shocked, and amused in reading these pages. In the form of an autobiography, it reads more like a story. This is not surprising, of course, since it was written by one of the masters of storytelling of the twentieth century. In reading his story, we are reminded of characters or situations from his many books, and we see how he was able to turn his own wealth of experiences into fiction. We are amazed once again at his incredible imagination. We are also amazed to learn that his first language as a child was not English, although all of his schooling was in English. It may be that the author's bilingual childhood gave him a special appreciation for the English language. In any case, we are delighted not only by the people and events he describes in this book, but also by the way in which he describes them.

    a. What is the reviewer's opinion of this book?

    _____

    b. How do you know?

    _____

Unit 10: **Summarizing**

❖ **Summarizing sentences**

Test 1

➤ *Summarize these sentences. Use as few words as possible to state the main point of each sentence.*

1. Driving slowly through the snowy hills, the Baskin family sang songs and ate snacks as they traveled up windy roads to the mountaintop ski lodge that they visited every year at Christmas.

   Summary: _____

2. Jeff slowed down the car, pulled over to the side of the road in a safe spot, turned off the engine, opened the door, walked to the back of the car, and opened the trunk, to look for the jack and the spare tire.

   Summary: _____

3. Until recently, the Hudson River, one of America's most beautiful waterways, stretching 350 miles from the Adirondack Mountains to Manhattan, was polluted with municipal waste, industrial chemicals, and farm drainage, but today the Hudson is full of life.

   Summary: _____

4. At a special meeting of the school board, the president praised the Nevada High School students for taking first prize in the national chess, debate, science, and math competitions, as well as winning the basketball and football state championships.

   Summary: _____

5. Dangerous wind storms in Western Europe, floods and mudslides in Venezuela, very dry conditions in U.S. farm regions, multiple hurricanes, overflowing rivers, and unusual heat and cold are all considered to be possible effects of global warming according to some scientists and observers.

   Summary: _____

Unit 10: **Summarizing**

❖ **Summarizing sentences**

Test 2

➤ *Summarize these sentences. Use as few words as possible to state the main point of each sentence.*

1. On the last day of the semester, students in the English class brought Italian pasta dishes, Russian borscht, Chinese noodles, Cuban vegetables, Japanese sushi, and Moroccan chicken, and the teacher brought American-style desserts including strawberry shortcake, chocolate chip cookies, and ice cream.

   Summary: _____

2. The computers in the library at North Shore Community College can help you find books, magazines, newspapers, CDs, videos, reference materials, and information about other colleges and universities.

   Summary: _____

3. Slowly and quietly, Yoshi unlocked the door of his house and walked softly up the dark stairs, being careful not to wake up his wife, Miho, his children, Tomiko and Yazu, and most importantly the big family dog, Zero.

   Summary: _____

4. After the family finished eating dinner, it was the children's job to clear the table, put away the food, load the dishwasher, wash the pots and pans, and take out the garbage.

   Summary: _____

5. When he arrived in Brazil to teach English, John had to find an apartment, buy a car, find out where to buy food, get the telephone installed, and buy some new furniture.

   Summary: _____

Unit 10: **Summarizing**

❖ **Summarizing short passages**

Test 1

➤ *Summarize this short passage. Follow the steps below.*

The Disappearing Rain Forests

A rain forest is a dense forest of evergreen trees that gets at least 2.5 meters (100 inches) of rain every year. The fact that it rains so much makes these forests different from others. There are many more species of plant and animal life in rain forests, which makes them very valuable to scientists. From the new species they discover in rain forests, medical scientists have been able to make new medicines that may save many people's lives. Environmentalists have shown that rain forests are necessary to clean the Earth's air, removing carbon dioxide and adding oxygen.

In spite of all of this information about their importance, people are cutting down the trees in tropical and northern rain forests. Some people want to use the land for farming. Others, owners of logging companies, are cutting down the rain forests to sell the wood. Around the world, trees have been cut down in almost 80 percent of the Earth's original rain forests, and large areas of these forests have disappeared.

In many of the remaining rain forests, the logging companies are still at work cutting trees. In the northern rain forests, this means cutting very old trees. The trees in these forests grow very slowly, but they for live a long time. In the Great Bear rain forest in western Canada, for example, some of the trees are over a thousand years old. Once they are cut down, of course, they cannot be replaced.

The logging companies argue that using the wood from these forests is necessary. The wood is sold as lumber for building houses and making furniture. The leftover pieces of wood are sold to companies that make paper products or cellulose. Cellulose is used in making many things, from toothpaste to pills. Scientists and environmentalists, however, view the situation very differently. They believe that it is not necessary to cut down the rain forests in order to make paper or toothpaste. They believe it is more important to preserve the rain forests in order to preserve life on planet Earth.

Step 1: Write one sentence to summarize each paragraph. Use as few words as possible.

Paragraph 1: _____

Paragraph 2: _____

Paragraph 3: _____

Paragraph 4: _____

Step 2: Now tie the sentences together to make one short paragraph. Write the final summary on a separate sheet of paper.

Unit 10: **Summarizing**

❖ **Summarizing short passages**

Test 2

➤ *Summarize this short passage. Follow the steps below.*

Ravens

The raven is a large, black, and very intelligent bird. There are many stories about the clever things it will do to get food. In one story, for example, a raven stole a picnic lunch from a man hiking in the woods in Canada during the winter. The man left his bag for a few minutes while he went to get some wood for a fire. When he came back he found the bag open. His sunglasses, gloves, and other things were out in the snow. Nearby, a raven was finishing off the man's sandwich and two chocolate bars. In order to get the food, the raven had to open three zippers in the bag.

A visitor at a hotel, also in Canada, saw two ravens use a different method to get food. One morning she heard a dog barking loudly. When she looked out the window, she saw the dog jumping and pulling at the chain that tied him to his doghouse. In front of him was one of the ravens, just far enough away so the dog couldn't reach it. The poor dog barked and barked as the raven flapped its wings and made loud noises. While the dog was barking at the first raven, the second raven was eating the dog's food in the doghouse! After a few minutes, the two ravens changed places. Once they had both eaten, they flew away.

Ravens also use their intelligence to help them live in the very cold Canadian climate. In one small town in the Yukon, the temperature in winter can go to minus 45 degrees Celsius. For ravens, as for other animals, keeping warm is a problem. If they cannot find a warm place, they may freeze and die. So what do ravens do to keep warm? They use the streetlights as heaters. Modern streetlights have light sensors that tell the lights to turn on when it is dark. Normally, the streetlights are off during the day, but some ravens have learned to sit on the lights and cover them with their wings. This action makes the lights turn on, and the heat from the lights keeps the ravens warm.

Ravens also show their intelligence in their ability to "speak." Ravens have sometimes been kept as pets and taught to say words. One family in Texas had a very intelligent pet raven for 25 years. It could copy the sounds of the family's voices and say their names. In fact, the children often couldn't tell whether it was their mother calling or the raven.

Step 1: Write one sentence to summarize each paragraph. Use as few words as possible.

Paragraph 1: _____

Paragraph 2: _____

Paragraph 3: _____

Paragraph 4: _____

Step 2: Now tie the sentences together to make one short paragraph. Write the final summary on a separate sheet of paper.

Unit 10: Summarizing

❖ Summarizing short passages

Test 3

➤ **Summarize this short passage. Follow the steps given on the next page.**

Harry Wu

Harry Wu was born in China in 1937. While he was studying at the university, he became interested in the problems of his country. He did not agree with some of the decisions of the Chinese government. One day, he expressed this opinion in a classroom discussion, and he was arrested for being against the government. Because of what he said, he was sent to jail for 19 years. In prison, he was forced to work hard digging coal in small caves underground. At last, when Harry was released from prison in 1976, he returned to study at the university. He said that he felt free of the small caves, but that his homeland was like a large cave—closed and dark.

Harry became an expert geologist and, in 1985, he was offered an opportunity to work at the University of California at Berkley. In the United States, he felt free, even though he made very little money. He got a second job as a night worker in a 24-hour doughnut shop, which gave him a place to spend the night and food to eat. Harry promised himself that he would forget about the past misery in China and start a new life in America. He wanted to go to the beach. He wanted money, a car, a house, and a new life. He wanted to get married. He was just like millions of other immigrants who came to America to start over again.

However, Harry was unable to forget his past. He tried to want the good things in life, but he said, "I could not do it. I had no choice." Harry remembered all the people, like himself, who suffered in China because they wanted to speak up against the Chinese government. He decided that what he really wanted, more than a good life for himself, was more freedom for China. What that meant was fighting the same government that put him in prison in order to help the Chinese people gain more freedom and greater human rights.

Harry has done just what he set out to do. He has written books and articles about Chinese prisons. He started an organization to inform Americans about the terrible conditions in Chinese prisons. He wants Americans to know how the Chinese government makes money from the products that its prisoners are forced to make. Since he became an American citizen, Harry Wu has returned to China several times. The Chinese government wanted to put him back in prison for his activities, but they could not do it because of his U.S. citizenship. To the Chinese, Harry has been a "troublemaker," but he is proud of this name. In fact, *Troublemaker* is the title of his book about human rights in China.

Step 1: *Write one sentence to summarize each paragraph. Use as few words as possible.*

Paragraph 1: _____

Paragraph 2: _____

Paragraph 3: _____

Paragraph 4: _____

Step 2: *Now tie the sentences together to make one short paragraph. Write the final summary below.*

Unit 10: **Summarizing**

❖ **Summarizing longer passages**

Test 1

➤ **Summarize the article, "Water Sports in Hawaii." Follow the steps below for summarizing a longer passage.**

Step 1: Read the passage all the way through.

Step 2: Go back to the beginning and number the paragraphs in the text.

Step 3: Divide the text into parts. Notice which paragraphs focus on the same idea. Part 1, for example, will be paragraph #1 to paragraph # "x." (You may not need to use all of these parts.)

Part 1: Paragraph 1–_____

Part 2: Paragraph _____–_____

Part __: Paragraph _____–_____

Part __: Paragraph _____–_____

Part __: Paragraph _____–_____

Step 4: For each part, write a sentence that summarizes all the paragraphs in it.

Part 1: _____

Part 2: _____

Part _____: _____

Part _____: _____

Part _____: _____

Step 5: Tie all of those sentences together to form a one-paragraph summary, using signal words and other function words. Use as few words as possible.

Water Sports in Hawaii

If you enjoy water sports, Hawaii is the place for you! You can go swimming all year round in the warm water. You can go sport fishing from the shore or from a boat. If you like boats, you can go sailing, canoeing, or windsurfing. Or you can also try some other water sports that are especially popular in Hawaii: surfing, snorkeling, and scuba diving.

Surfing is a sport which started in Hawaii many years ago. The Hawaiians called it "he'enalu," which means "to slide on a wave." Long before the arrival of the Europeans, the Hawaiians would ride on the waves on long, narrow wooden boards. When the first Europeans came to the islands, they were amazed by these surfing Hawaiians. Since that time, surfing has become a very popular sport on the California coast and in Australia, among other places.

If you want to try surfing, you need, first of all, to be a good swimmer. You also have to have an excellent sense of balance. You must swim out from the beach with your surfboard under your arm. When you get to where the waves begin to break, you wait for a calm moment. Then you try to stand up on the board. The wave will begin to rise under you. You must try to steer the board with your feet so you stay on top of the wave. The important thing is to keep your balance and not fall down. If you can manage this, you will have an exciting ride all the way in to the shore.

Scuba diving and snorkeling are two ways to get a close look at the beauty lying below the surface of the ocean. The waters off the Hawaiian Islands are clean, clear, and warm. They contain hundreds of kinds of colorful fish. The undersea world is made even more colorful by the coral reefs of red, gold, white, and light purple. Among these reefs there may be larger fish or sea turtles.

Scuba diving allows you to see the most interesting undersea sights. "SCUBA" means "Self-Contained Underwater Breathing Apparatus," that is, equipment for breathing and swimming around far under water. In Hawaii, you can take special courses to learn how to scuba dive. After the courses, you can get a certificate that will allow you to dive alone. Since it can be dangerous, proper instruction and great care are always necessary when you are scuba diving.

If you are less adventurous, you might try snorkeling instead of scuba diving. Less equipment is needed, just a face mask, a breathing tube (snorkel), and flippers for your feet. It only takes a few minutes to learn how to snorkel. Although you cannot dive deep into the water, you can swim with your face below the surface. Breathing through the tube, you float on the surface and keep yourself moving with your flippers. Even from the surface like this, there will be plenty of color and beauty to see.

Unit 10: **Summarizing**

❖ **Summarizing longer passages**

Test 2

➤ *Summarize the article, "Overcoming Jet Lag." Follow the steps below for summarizing a longer passage.*

Step 1: **Read the passage all the way through.**

Step 2: **Go back to the beginning and number the paragraphs in the text.**

Step 3: **Divide the text into parts. Notice which paragraphs focus on the same idea. Part 1, for example, will be paragraph #1 to paragraph # "x". (You may not need to use all of these parts.)**

Part 1: Paragraph 1–_____

Part 2: Paragraph _____–_____

Part __: Paragraph _____–_____

Part __: Paragraph _____–_____

Part __: Paragraph _____–_____

Step 4: **For each part, write a sentence that summarizes all the paragraphs in it.**

Part 1: _____

Part 2: _____

Part _____: _____

Part _____: _____

Part _____: _____

Step 5: **Tie all of those sentences together to form a one-paragraph summary, using signal words and other function words. Use as few words as possible.**

Overcoming Jet Lag

Experts give recommendations on what works and what doesn't in trying to escape the effects of crossing time zones.

BY MONICA BROOKS

The day before a long flight you are frantically doing last-minute chores and errands, packing, and reading guide books. Then, on the plane, you have several drinks with dinner and stay up late watching the movie. After a brief nap, it's time for breakfast and a morning arrival in, let's say, Paris or Rome. Adrenaline flowing, you spend the entire day sightseeing and taking pictures. By evening, exhaustion has set in, and the next morning, you can hardly wake up before noon. Jet lag has taken hold.

Most people who travel by air across multiple time zones fall victim to this affliction of modern air travel. They may suffer from any of a number of unpleasant symptoms, including insomnia, fatigue, nausea, sleepiness, and lethargy.

According to Dr. Harriet Minsky, professor of psychology at Montreal University, the symptoms of jet lag vary from person to person, and also vary according to how far a traveler has flown. Recovery from jet lag also varies, with some sufferers feeling better gradually and others experiencing alternative days of feeling better or worse.

Dr. Minsky points out that there are three primary causes of jet lag, and of these, two are avoidable. First, people often wear themselves out getting ready for a trip, so they are already exhausted when they get on the plane. Second, long-distance travelers often have a couple of drinks to pass the time. The alcohol can cause stomach distress and interfere with getting a good night's sleep.

The third and unavoidable cause of jet lag is the fact that long-distance air travel upsets your internal biological clock. Dr. Alvin Lacy, chief of general medicine at Northern Medical College, explains that our inner clock controls our cycle of sleeping and waking.

The brain takes its cues from the amount of light and other features in the environment. Without environmental cues, the brain tends to set its biological clock to a longer day. This means that, for most travelers, the effects of jet lag are less severe on trips toward the west, because the travel is following the sun. In traveling toward the east, the body must adjust by shortening its day, going against the body's natural tendency. This explains why trips from west to east often result in greater suffering from jet lag.

Individuals are not all affected to the same degree by jet lag. For example, "night owls," people who are usually most alert and lively at night, are less likely to feel the effects of jet lag. Younger people suffer less than older travelers. In terms of personality types, extroverts (people who are sociable and like to be in groups) tend to suffer less than introverts.

Many people believe that there must be some quick and easy cure for jet lag—and, in fact, all kinds of cures have been popularized, from vitamins to special diets, but research has shown that none of these is very effective.

However, Dr. Minsky assures travelers that if they follow certain common sense strategies, they will overcome jet lag more quickly.

- Get plenty of rest and eat healthy meals prior to taking a long flight.

- On the plane, set your watch to your destination's time immediately. Then allow that time to guide your behavior. During the trip, eat and sleep according to the new time zone.

- Once you arrive, begin to follow a normal routine for that time zone. Try not to take naps. Set an alarm clock to wake you in the morning. Spend time outside during the day, and sleep at night.

- Avoid sleeping pills, alcohol, or other drugs that you do not normally use.

Part Three

Evaluating Thinking Skills

These tests follow the same format as the Thinking Skills exercises in the Student Book. Thinking Skills exercises help students concentrate and think in English, at the same time giving them practice in many aspects of the thinking processes that are activated while reading: making inferences, guessing the meaning of new vocabulary, noticing relationship patterns, and reading critically. The difficulty of the exercises increases gradually as the student progresses through them.

There are three levels of Thinking Skills tests, with three tests provided at each level. It is important to give the tests after completing the appropriate Thinking Skills exercises in the Student Book.

Level One Tests: Give after students have completed Exercises 1–35
                     (pages 181–188) in their book.
Level Two Tests: Give after students have completed Exercises 36–70
                     (pages 188–197) in their book.
Level Three Tests: Give after students have completed Exercises 71–100
                     (pages 197–204) in their book.

Students should complete the Thinking Skills tests without using a dictionary.

Level One: **Evaluating Thinking Skills**

Test 1

➤ **Take this test after completing Exercises 1–35 in the Student Book (pages 181–188).**

Choose the best ending for each paragraph.

1. Elmhurst is a part of Queens, in New York City. It has always been a very mixed neighborhood, with people from many different countries. Recently, it has become even more mixed, with many new immigrants. In fact, in the 1990s it became the most mixed neighborhood in the United States. In those years, people came to Elmhurst from
    - ❏ a. New York City.
    - ❏ b. five other countries.
    - ❏ c. over one hundred countries.
    - ❏ d. other parts of the United States.

2. Did you know that the music played in a store can make a difference in your shopping? You may not think about the music at all, but it still can change your behavior. If a store plays music that is typical of a country, you are more likely to buy something from that country. In a wine store with French music, for example, you will probably buy
    - ❏ a. French wine.
    - ❏ b. French cheese.
    - ❏ c. lots of wine.
    - ❏ d. American wine.

3. Jenny Lind was a singer in the nineteenth century. Though she came from Sweden, she became famous all around the world for her beautiful voice. She was known as the Swedish Nightingale. The name comes from the fact that the nightingale, a small bird,
    - ❏ a. is Swedish.
    - ❏ b. travels around the world.
    - ❏ c. sings only rarely.
    - ❏ d. sings very beautifully.

4. Living in a small town can be a good thing. Everyone knows each other well and can help each other in times of trouble. Sometimes there is also a bad side to small town life, though. You may feel that people are always watching you and
    - ❏ a. wondering what to do.
    - ❏ b. talking about you.
    - ❏ c. welcoming you.
    - ❏ d. listening to the radio.

5. Going to the dentist is nothing new. In Colorado, scientists found bones and teeth that were 2,000 years old. One of the teeth had a hole in it. It had clearly been made with the purpose of trying to take care of the teeth. In fact, it looked just like the holes that
    - ❏ a. can be found in all old teeth.
    - ❏ b. dentists find in teeth today.
    - ❏ c. dentists make in teeth today.
    - ❏ d. can be found in dentists' teeth.

Level One: **Evaluating Thinking Skills**

Test 2

➤ **Take this test after completing Exercises 1–35 in the Student Book (pages 181–188).**

Choose the best ending for each paragraph.

1.　　The longest train line in the world is the Trans-Siberian railway. Its 5,770 miles of track connects Moscow in Russia with Vladivostok in Russian Siberia (on the Pacific coast). The trip takes about 6 days and 12 hours. This may seem like a long time, but it's much better than driving! There is no highway from Moscow to Vladivostok. In some areas, there are no roads at all, except in winter. Then the roads are

  ❏ a. not open.　　　　　　　　　　❏ c. on the railroad.

  ❏ b. on open water.　　　　　　　　❏ d. made on ice.

2.　　On the Orkney Islands, off the coast of Scotland, there is almost always a lot of wind. This means you have to lean forward into the wind when you are walking so it won't blow you over. In fact, everyone on the islands walks around leaning far over into the wind. People from the islands like to joke about this. They say that one day the wind will suddenly stop and

  ❏ a. everyone will fall over.　　　　　❏ c. everyone will keep walking.

  ❏ b. it will begin to rain.　　　　　　❏ d. no one will notice.

3.　　Jacques-Yves Cousteau, a Frenchman, was a famous explorer. On television and in films, he showed viewers a whole new world under the sea. He was able to do this partly because of his invention, the Aqua-Lung. This machine allowed people to breathe underwater. They could swim around deep underwater and

  ❏ a. had to come to the surface for air.　　❏ c. travel around the world.

  ❏ b. stay there for a long time.　　　　　❏ d. close their eyes.

4.　　Two thousand years ago, the Nabataeans lived in the southern desert of present-day Jordan. These people built a city called Petra. It was the most important trading center in this part of the Middle East. It had beautiful temples, theaters, and other buildings. It also had water. The Nabataeans had made a complicated system that brought water to the city from the mountains. Without this water, Petra would

  ❏ a. still be important.　　　　　　　❏ c. never have been a small village.

  ❏ b. not be in the Middle East.　　　　❏ d. never have become so important.

5.　　Amber is a yellowish-brown stone often used in jewelry. It takes millions of years for it to form. First, it was a kind of liquid, called resin, produced by certain plants or trees. Then over time, the liquid became a hard stone. Sometimes you can find pieces of plants, flowers, or even insects in these stones. From these, scientists can get important information about

  ❏ a. how to make valuable jewelry.　　❏ c. the natural world millions of years
  ❏ b. plants and trees in our world　　　　　ago.
     today.　　　　　　　　　　　　❏ d. how people lived millions of years
  　　　　　　　　　　　　　　　　　　ago.

Level One: Evaluating Thinking Skills

Test 3

➤ **Take this test after completing Exercises 1–35 in the Student Book (pages 181–188).**

Choose the best ending for each paragraph.

1.   The rose is one of the best-loved flowers of all time. People love their many beautiful colors and their wonderful smell. The only problem with roses is that they have thorns—sharp points along the branches. In fact, there is an old saying, "Every rose has its thorns." By this, people mean that
   ❏ a. some roses are not so beautiful.   ❏ c. thorns are beautiful, too.
   ❏ b. some beautiful things may hurt you.   ❏ d. beautiful things can be perfect.

2.   Scientists have long been looking for the key to a long life. Now they realize there is no magic solution that will keep everyone alive and healthy for a long time. They are, however, learning more about aging. They know, for example, that people who live to be 80 or 90 usually do not eat more than necessary. In fact, they are almost never overweight. So, if you want to live a long life,
   ❏ a. eat all you want.   ❏ c. eat more than necessary.
   ❏ b. do not eat any meat.   ❏ d. do not become overweight.

3.   Accidents are one of the most common causes of death among children. Most of these accidents happen at home and most of them could be prevented. Some countries, such as Great Britain, have been working to prevent accidents in the home. Thanks to their prevention programs, in the past 15 years, the number of accidents in Great Britain has
   ❏ a. gone down by 47 percent.   ❏ c. stayed the same.
   ❏ b. gone up by 47 percent.   ❏ d. multiplied by 3.

4.   It is no news that smoking cigarettes is bad for your health. Millions of people continue to smoke, however, and continue to suffer from diseases caused by smoking. Every year in the United States alone about 400,000 people die from these diseases. The yearly cost to the U.S. government is billions of dollars. Many people are beginning to think that smoking is also
   ❏ a. bad for their country.   ❏ c. an inexpensive pleasure.
   ❏ b. good for their country.   ❏ d. bad for their teeth.

5.   An American traveling in England needs to be careful when shopping for clothes. Quite a few words have different meanings in American or British English. For example, to Americans, a vest is a sleeveless sweater or jacket that goes over your shirt. In England, on the other hand, it's an undershirt. Similarly, to an American, pants are outerwear, the same as trousers. In England, however, pants are worn under trousers and generally not
   ❏ a. worn at all.   ❏ c. shown in public.
   ❏ b. known in Ireland.   ❏ d. bought in stores.

Level Two: **Evaluating Thinking Skills**

Test 1

➤ **Take this test after completing Exercises 36–70 in the Student Book (pages 188–197).**

Choose the best ending for each paragraph.

1.   Alvar Aalto, an architect from Finland, lived from 1898 to 1976. He is known for the beautiful public buildings and private houses, as well as furniture and objects, that he designed. Aalto got many of his ideas for designs from the beautiful countryside around him. For example, the idea for the shape of a glass vase came from

    ❏ a. reading a book.   ❏ c. looking at a lake.
    ❏ b. speaking to a friend.   ❏ d. thinking about the future.

2.   The dance music in *Swan Lake,* written in 1876 by Tchaikovsky, is still very popular today. Since its first performance in Russia, it has been performed many times by classical dance companies around the world. In one famous dance, there is a group of swans—large white birds. These swans have always been danced by women in white dresses. At a recent performance in England, however, the audience had a big surprise. The swans were completely different. They

    ❏ a. were danced by athletic men in black. ❏ c. were danced by Russian women.
    ❏ b. didn't dance well.   ❏ d. had short white dresses.

3.   After the age of about 40—in middle age—your eyes can change. You may still be able to see road signs perfectly well when you are driving, but you may not be able to focus well on things that are close to you. When you are reading, for example, you may have to hold the book far away from you. This is the only way you can focus on the print. At this point your eye doctor may tell you to get

    ❏ a. protective glasses.   ❏ c. driving glasses.
    ❏ b. sunglasses.   ❏ d. reading glasses.

4.   Butterflies are beautiful to watch as they fly from flower to flower with their colorful wings. Now scientists in California have found another reason to watch butterflies. They have discovered that these insects are very sensitive to changes in climate. If the temperature gets warmer, they move north. If it gets colder, they move south. In recent years, the scientists have noticed that many California butterflies now live farther north than they used to. This probably means that the climate in California

    ❏ a. has gotten colder.   ❏ c. has not changed.
    ❏ b. has gotten warmer.   ❏ d. is not good for them.

5.   The wolf and the dog are cousins in the animal world. In many ways, they are very similar in their appearance and behavior. People have sometimes put a wolf and dog together to get a puppy that is half wolf and half dog. These puppies may not make good pets, however. For example, one of these puppies once heard a sound coming from a sofa spring. She thought it was a mouse, so she tore apart the sofa to try to get it. In this case, the puppy's behavior was

    ❏ a. wolf-like.   ❏ c. human.
    ❏ b. dog-like.   ❏ d. suitable.

Level Two: **Evaluating Thinking Skills**

Test 2

➤ *Take this test after completing Exercises 36–70 in the Student Book (pages 188–197).*

Choose the best ending for each paragraph.

1.　　When the *Titanic* left England on April 14, 1912, everyone thought the ship was unsinkable. The captain was so sure about this that he was not very careful. He made the ship go faster than usual in an area with many icebergs. This extra speed was an important factor in the disaster. If the ship had been going more slowly, it might have been able to
    ❏ a. hit the iceberg harder.
    ❏ b. reach New York sooner.
    ❏ c. go around the iceberg.
    ❏ d. sink more slowly.

2.　　In 1997, the Red River flooded Grand Forks, North Dakota. In the downtown area, the water was very deep. This flooding caused a lot of electrical damage, which, in turn, caused fires. It was difficult for the firemen to get to the buildings because of the deep water, and, in the end, eleven buildings were destroyed. In fact, it must have been a strange situation for the firemen. There they were, fighting fires
    ❏ a. with water all around them.
    ❏ b. in a city.
    ❏ c. while the buildings burned.
    ❏ d. with no water.

3.　　Scientists believe that birds developed from dinosaurs. The first dinosaur-birds could not fly, but they could move their front legs up and down like wings. Later bird-like animals had feathers but still couldn't fly. According to evidence, the ability to fly dates to about 115 million years ago. At about that time, birds developed special feathers on their wings. These feathers made it possible for them to control their wings in the air. This was the
    ❏ a. beginning of the dinosaur era.
    ❏ b. end of birds as we know them.
    ❏ c. beginning of modern history.
    ❏ d. beginning of birds as we know them.

4.　　Alfred Hitchcock, the movie director, made movies with many different actors. There is something similar about all of his films, though. In fact, if you are familiar with Hitchcock, it is easy to recognize one of his movies. They all have a similar mixture of funny moments and very scary moments. They also have a special "look"—a way of shooting the movie—that
    ❏ a. was Hitchcock's name.
    ❏ b. depended on the actors.
    ❏ c. was Hitchcock's style.
    ❏ d. was different every time.

5.　　In recent years, the high rate of immigration to the United States has brought changes to American schools. More and more of the children in school come from families whose first language is not English. In two states, Texas and California, there are now more students from non-English-speaking families than from
    ❏ a. non-English-speaking states.
    ❏ b. Spanish-speaking families.
    ❏ c. English-speaking families.
    ❏ d. immigrant families.

Level Two: **Evaluating Thinking Skills**

Test 3

➤ **Take this test after completing Exercises 36–70 in the Student Book (pages 188–197).**

Choose the best ending for each paragraph.

1. "An apple a day keeps the doctor away." This old saying used to be very popular with mothers to help persuade their children to eat fruit. In the past, people thought that apples were good for you, but they did not know why. Now we know that apples are in fact very good for your general health, like all fruit. We also know that eating apples regularly can help people with heart trouble and with high cholesterol levels. Perhaps we should pay more attention to what our mothers used to say! Old sayings

    ❑ a. are never true.
    ❑ b. tell us to eat more.
    ❑ c. can hold some truth.
    ❑ d. do not make sense.

2. Trieste is a city in northeastern Italy. For most of the eighteenth and nineteenth centuries, however, Trieste was not an Italian city. It was part of the Austro-Hungarian Empire. As the only seaport on the Mediterranean Sea, Trieste became an important center for Austrian shipping and trade. It was also an important cultural center, especially at the beginning of the twentieth century, when it was the home of many famous writers. Now Trieste is a small, quiet city and the port is no longer important. Tourists enjoy it because of the seaside location and the many beautiful

    ❑ a. English-style buildings.
    ❑ b. Austrian-style buildings.
    ❑ c. German-style industries.
    ❑ d. American-style skyscrapers.

3. At the beginning of the twentieth century, the world population was about 2 billion. At the end of the century, it had grown to 6 billion. Some scientists believe that by the year 2050 there will be 10.6 billion people in the world. Others think population growth will be slower and there will be only 7.3 billion people. Most scientists agree, however, that the rate of growth will depend on the conditions for women around the world. If women everywhere can choose the size of their families, population growth will be slower. If they do not have a choice, the population of the world will

    ❑ a. stay the same.
    ❑ b. reach 6 billion.
    ❑ c. slow down.
    ❑ d. grow more quickly.

4. In many places around the world, people depend on fishing. Some people fish for food for their families, since fish is traditionally an important part of the diet. Other people sell the fish they catch in local markets. Still others work in the fishing industry, on big boats or in fish-processing factories. The fishing industry, in fact, has grown enormously over the past half century. It may have grown too much. At present, scientists think that about 70 percent of the fish in our oceans are in danger of disappearing completely. The reason for this is simple:

    ❑ a. too much fishing
    ❑ b. too many fish
    ❑ c. not enough fishing
    ❑ d. too many people

5.   In the book business, people talk about two kinds of best-sellers. There is the "blockbuster" written by a well-known author. These books get a lot of publicity in the media and in the bookstores, and they sell many copies immediately. There is also the "sleeper," a very different kind of book. It is often written by an unknown author and is publicized very little. At first, the sleeper sells very few copies, but some people really like it and talk about it. As more and more people read it, it becomes better known. Finally, the media and big bookstores learn about it and

❏ a. only a few copies are sold.   ❏ c. buy some copies.
❏ b. tell people not to read it.   ❏ d. many copies are sold.

Level Three: **Evaluating Thinking Skills**

Test 1

➤ **Take this test after completing Exercises 71–100 in the Student Book (pages 197–204).**

Choose the best ending for each paragraph.

1.   At the beginning of Tolstoy's novel *Anna Karenina,* we learn about the Oblonsky family. "Everything was in confusion" in the house and everyone in the family was unhappy. The novel goes on to tell the reader all about this situation. Most of Tolstoy's novels focus on life's troubles and tragedies. He thought they were more interesting. As he wrote in the first sentence to *Anna Karenina,* "Happy families are all alike; every unhappy family

❑ a. is also happy."   ❑ c. lives in Russia."

❑ b. is unhappy in its own way."   ❑ d. is boring to read about."

2.   Many people think that a child from a bilingual family—a family where two languages are spoken—will be different from other children. They think that he or she will learn to speak later than children in families with only one language. However, studies show this is not true. A child from a bilingual family

❑ a. learns to speak at the same age as   ❑ c. learns to understand many
          other children.   different languages.

❑ b. doesn't ever learn to speak.   ❑ d. learns to speak only one language.

3.   Breakfast cereals were first made in the United States by Dr. Joseph Kellogg in the 1890s. As a doctor, he thought that the usual American breakfast was too large and rich. In those days, it was usually a full meal with meat, eggs, and bread. He also knew that many people didn't have much time in the morning, so he invented Corn Flakes. They soon became popular in the United States because they are

❑ a. heavy and rich.   ❑ c. made without eggs.

❑ b. very expensive.   ❑ d. quick and light.

4.   Giorgio Casadio, from Ravenna, Italy, got his first driver's license in 1917 at the age of 22. He has been driving ever since. He renewed his license yet again in 1992—at the age of 97. Since he was the oldest person ever to renew a driver's license in Italy, there was an article about him in the newspaper. He told the newspaper reporter that he hoped to continue his good driving record. In 75 years of driving he had

❑ a. had many accidents.   ❑ c. never driven a sports car.

❑ b. always worn glasses.   ❑ d. never had an accident.

5.   The first person to reach the South Pole was Roald Amundsen, a Norwegian, in 1911. He arrived at the Pole just days before Robert Scot, a Scotsman. Amundsen had prepared his trip very carefully, and he arrived safely back at the base camp. Scot was less prepared. He and several of his men died of cold and hunger. Strangely, however, of the two explorers, Scot became much more famous. People still think of him as a hero, while

❏ a. Amundsen's name is almost unknown.

❏ b. Amundsen is much loved.

❏ c. Amundsen's name is better known.

❏ d. Amundsen came from Norway.

Level Three: **Evaluating Thinking Skills**

Test 2

➤ **Take this test after completing Exercises 71–100 in the Student Book (pages 197–204).**

Choose the best ending for each paragraph.

1. The Caspian Sea is a small sea that borders on five countries, including Iran and Russia. For some reason that scientists do not understand, the water level of the sea does not always stay the same. It may go up or down by as much as eight feet in a few years. These changes may be caused by the flow of water into the sea, or they may be caused by other, unknown factors. In any case, in recent years, the water level has been rising. Some villages built along the coast are now

   ❏ a. in another country.   ❏ c. farther from the water.
   ❏ b. partly under water.   ❏ d. without water.

2. The wild dog has a lot in common with the wolf. It, too, is a member of the dog family. Like the wolf, it lives and hunts in groups. As with wolves, there are very strong rules for all the animals in the group. Another similarity with wolves is the way wild dogs have been hunted by men. Wolves used to be common in much of North America, but they are now very rare. The same is true of wild dogs. A century ago European explorers found wild dogs in most of southern Africa, but now there

   ❏ a. aren't any wild dogs.   ❏ c. are wild dogs in only a few places.
   ❏ b. are wild dogs only in North America.   ❏ d. are more wild dogs than before.

3. Charles Darwin was not the first person to visit the Galapagos Islands. Spanish sailors and explorers had been to the islands in the 1500s, and there is evidence that other humans had been there 600 years earlier. It was Darwin, however, who recognized the scientific importance of the islands. In fact, his experience there was a key moment in his life and work, and his observations there helped him write *The Origin of Species.* The reason for Darwin's interest in the islands was very simple. Many of the species of plants, animals, and insects he found there did not exist anywhere else, so the islands were a perfect place

   ❏ a. for hunting.   ❏ c. for writing a book.
   ❏ b. to study human development.   ❏ d. to study how species develop.

4.   Over a hundred years ago, some people brought goats to the Galapagos Islands. These people were farmers who wanted fresh milk and meat from the goats. Over time, some of the goats got away from the farmers. There was food for the goats and lots of wild space. Since there were no wolves or other animals to hunt them, the goats lived and multiplied. Now there are almost 200,000 on the two biggest islands, and these goats are a problem. The islands are famous with scientists and tourists for their giant sea tortoises—a kind of turtle. The problem is that the goats eat all the grass on the islands and leave no hiding places for the tortoises to lay their eggs. To solve this problem, the government has decided to

❑ a. plant more grass.
❑ b. hunt and kill the goats.
❑ c. sell the goat milk and meat.
❑ d. move the tortoises somewhere else.

5.   The basic job of a detective has not changed in the last hundred years. When someone is killed, the detective has to try to find the killer. This basic job was true for Sherlock Holmes in Arthur Conan Doyle's famous stories set in nineteenth-century England, and it's true for a detective today. However, there have been some important changes in the way a detective does his job. Today's detective can use modern technology—computers, the Internet, and genetics such as DNA fingerprinting—to help solve crimes. Holmes, on the other hand, had only his assistant, Dr. Watson, to help him. Mostly, he used his own very good eyes and ears and

❑ a. quick thinking.
❑ b. the telephone.
❑ c. detective stories.
❑ d. clothes.

More Reading Power Test Booklet

Level Three: **Evaluating Thinking Skills**

Test 3

➤ **Take this test after completing Exercises 71–100 in the Student Book (pages 197–204).**

Choose the best ending for each paragraph.

1.　　In the nineteenth century in England, women were not taken seriously as writers. Men at that time believed that women were not intelligent enough or strong enough to write books about serious subjects. They thought that women should only write books about "women's subjects," such as cooking or clothes. A number of women did write serious books in those years, though. Among these books were some of the best novels in English literature, including *Wuthering Heights, Jane Eyre,* and *Middlemarch.* In order to publish their books, however, the women who wrote them

　❑ a. also wrote cookbooks.　　❑ c. did not take themselves seriously.

　❑ b. used their own names.　　❑ d. had to use men's names.

2.　　The ostrich is the biggest bird in the world. It weighs as much as 350 pounds. These birds, originally from Africa, cannot fly, but they can run very fast. In the past, Europeans and Americans hunted ostriches for their feathers, which were long and beautiful and very popular for ladies' hats. Today, ostrich feathers are no longer popular, but there is new interest in ostriches for another reason—the meat. Ostrich meat has very little fat and is very good for you, according to doctors. There is also a lot of it on each bird, so some farmers in Texas and other places are now

　❑ a. raising many kinds of birds.　　❑ c. raising ostriches.

　❑ b. hunting ostriches.　　❑ d. selling ostrich feathers.

3.　　Scientists are learning a lot about the movement of populations from DNA research. For example, they have discovered that 90 percent of native South American men and 50 percent of native North Americans have the same genetic marker. This marker does not exist in any other male population. Scientists believe that it began with a change in the DNA of one man born about 15,000 to 20,000 years ago. This man may have been one of the first people to arrive in North America from Asia. Over the years, the population increased, and people moved into all of North and South America. This means that the majority of native Americans

　❑ a. are distant relatives of that 　　❑ c. are North American.
　　　 one man.　　　　　　　　　　　 ❑ d. do not have any genetic markers.

　❑ b. come from other countries.

4.   On June 6, 1924, George Mallory and Andrew Irvine started to climb Mount Everest in the Himalayan Mountains. Mallory, an Englishman, was a famous mountain climber, and Irvine had invented a new kind of oxygen bottle. These bottles could help mountain climbers breathe on very high mountains like Everest. Two days later, Mallory and Irvine disappeared and were never seen again. No one knew what had happened to them or whether they had managed to reach the top of the mountain. In 1999, a group of climbers found Mallory's body, but they could not solve the mystery of his death. Maybe no one will ever know why he died or if

❑ a. he was alive.

❑ b. he had used the oxygen.

❑ c. he had reached the top.

❑ d. it had been snowing.

5.   Some kinds of viruses are very tough. They can live through all kinds of conditions and for a very long time. That is why scientists in Egypt have to be careful when they are working with mummies. Mummies are the dried-up bodies of dead people. Even when the mummies are thousands of years old, they might carry live viruses. If a person breathes in the virus, it could become active again and could give you a disease that could even kill you. For this reason, scientists working with mummies

❑ a. live in Egypt.

❑ b. do not breathe.

❑ c. wear face masks.

❑ d. are never sick.

Evaluating Reading Faster

Some background information about Reading Faster

Before working on Part Four of the Student Book with students, it is important for teachers to have a good grasp of the rationale and objectives for the Reading Faster passages. This information can be found on page 297–299 in the Teacher's Guide at the end of the Student Book.

It is essential also that students understand how their reading rate relates to comprehension, and how regular practice with timed readings can help them learn to read faster. Thus, teachers should take special care in working through the Introduction to Part Four of the Student Book with students, taking the time to make sure that they understand fully the purpose of doing these exercises.

The effectiveness of the Reading Faster exercises depends on how the teacher approaches this work with the students. That is, students may tend to take this aspect of reading improvement less seriously than the comprehension skills exercises, or they may even refuse to accept the idea that learning to read faster is important. This attitude is partly because Part Four represents an approach to reading that may be novel to many students.

Why give grades on Reading Faster?

Students do need to be evaluated on their work and progress with the timed readings. Teachers need to know how students are progressing so they can intervene in order to encourage or to correct where necessary. Furthermore, some form of testing inevitably gives reading-rate-improvement exercises more importance in the eyes of the students.

In order to evaluate students' work in Part Four: Reading Faster, teachers will need to look at each student's individual effort and progress. This evaluation, of course, may be complicated by the fact that reading rate is dependent on the content of the reading materials. A student who is familiar with Hawaii, for example, might be able to read the passage in that unit very quickly. That same student, however, could find that his or her reading rate might slow down in the passages on Maria Montessori in the next unit. When this situation occurs, teachers will need to reassure students and explain to them how rate relates to content.

Guidelines for evaluating Reading Faster

Though the basis for evaluation must be tailored for each individual, the method for evaluating need not be subjective. The following guidelines are intended to provide teachers with suggestions for establishing a systematic method for evaluating and grading students' progress in reading-rate improvement.

1. Let the students know at the outset of the course that they will be evaluated on the basis of their individual progress, not in comparison to anyone else in the class or to some already-established score or rate.
2. Tell the students that they will receive either S (satisfactory) or U (unsatisfactory) for grades on their Reading Faster work. To receive a grade of "S," a student's reading rate on passages 9 and 10 of a unit as compared with passages 1 and 2 should show an increase of 10 percent or more, with acceptable comprehension scores (at least 6 correct).
3. At the first class meeting, the teacher should have the students tear out passages 9 and 10 in all three units in the Reading Faster section of their textbooks. The teacher should keep these passages and redistribute them when it is time to evaluate students' progress.
4. When the class has completed passage 8 in a unit, assign passages 9 and 10 for evaluation. The class is timed as usual, but without access to the textbook. After they have finished reading and answering the questions on a passage, the teacher should collect the passages and score them.
5. After correcting their answers and finding the students' reading rates, the teacher can compare students' work on the last two passages with their reading rate and comprehension scores on the first two passages, as recorded in their Progress Charts on page 274 of the Student Book.
6. Students who make an effort will usually show more than a 10 percent improvement in their reading rates. It is not uncommon for a student to double his or her reading rate in one semester.

Answer Key

Note: For purposes of scoring, each item equals 1 point.

Unit 1: Scanning

Test 1, page 8

1. West and Central equatorial Africa
2. 4.5 feet (1.3 meters)
3. 4 pounds (1.8 kilograms)
4. 50 years
5. 6 to 10
6. in the trees
7. fruits, vegetables, insects
8. swaying, stamping, screaming, throwing objects
9. rivers, because chimpanzees cannot swim
10. by solving problems, manipulating objects, making tools

Unit 2: Previewing and Predicting

Test 2, page 10

Answers for items 1–4 will vary.

1. how Sacagawea helped Lewis and Clark
2. 1804–1806, 1600 miles, $25 a month, age of 12, 29 Shoshone horses
3. Sacagawea, Shoshone, Jefferson, Charbonneau, Lewis, Clark
4. Louisiana, St. Louis, Pacific Ocean, North Dakota, Rocky Mountains, Missouri River, Columbia River
5. a. Jefferson
6. c. 1,500 miles
7. a. $25
8. a. token of peace
9. b. Missouri River
10. a. trade items for horses
11. b. tireless person
12. a. is an important figure in American history
13. c. symbolic pieces of jewelry
14. c. wanted to visit her original tribe

Unit 3: Vocabulary Knowledge for Effective Reading

Guessing meaning from context in sentences

In these tests, the answers may vary. The important thing is that students have good reasons for their answers.

Test 1, page 13
1. a beginner
2. expressed in a few words
3. careful about spending money
4. to cut wood with a tool
5. the bones of the head
6. to flow or move slowly (usually a thick liquid)

Test 2, page 14
1. a place where stone is dug or cut out of the ground
2. to become unpleasantly sharp-tasting and not good to eat or drink (especially milk products)
3. a person who helps you find a seat or takes your ticket in a theater
4. to argue about money
5. to produce more of a kind of animal
6. on a boat or ship

Test 3, page 15
1. very happy
2. without a home (usually a cat or dog)
3. an unwanted hole or crack in something, through which liquid or air can pass
4. a painful, raised place on the skin caused by repeated rubbing
5. to speak in a low voice to oneself, usually in a negative tone
6. because of this; therefore

Referents in a longer essay

Test 1, page 16

6	they—	the rocks
8	openings—	openings on the surface of the earth
9	They—	the mountains
10	This—	the mountains become tall enough to rise above the water and form islands
11	archipelago—	collection of islands
15	they—	the oldest islands
22	it—	an underwater volcano about 30 miles south of the island of Hawaii
22	this volcano—	the underwater volcano
25	there—	the islands
31	evolved—	changing to adapt themselves to their conditions
36	It—	about 1,500 years ago, the first humans arrived

Test 2, page 18

8	they—	their children
8	their—	the children's
12	its—	United States
17	they—	Florida residents
18	In this way—	study in bilingual education programs
22	their—	many states
23	the nation's—	the United States
24	their—	the American people
29	it—	English
32	countries—	Canada and Belgium
39	they—	opponents of the official English movement *or* the opposition

Unit 4: **Topics**

Working with the topic

Answers may vary. The important thing is that students have good reasons for their answers. The crossed-out words are in parentheses here.

Test 1, page 20
1. liquids you can drink (gasoline)
2. planets (Moon)
3. stringed instruments (clarinet)
4. countries in Asia (Hawaii)
5. western states of the United States (Massachusetts)
6. countries in Europe (Canada)

7. exercises that are done on land (swimming)
8. vegetables that grow underground (cucumbers)
9. languages (American)
10. geographical areas that are at least partly within the Arctic Circle (South Pole)

Test 2, page 22
1. elected leadership positions (king)
2. valuable stones (gold)
3. items of clothing that are spoken of in the plural (twins); things that come in twos (pants)
4. car makers outside of the United States (Ford)
5. kinds of cheese (vanilla)
6. food departments of a supermarket (Check-Out)
7. singers in English (Ricky Martin)
8. parts of a computer (copier)
9. things found at a beach (picnic)
10. kinds of boats without motors (speedboat)

Unit 5: **Topics of Paragraphs**

Stating the topic of a paragraph

Any similar answer is acceptable.

Test 1, page 24
1. the reasons why mollusks have shells
2. the differences between bivalves and univalves
3. some things to think about before collecting seashells

Test 2, page 25
1. Teresa Weatherspoon, famous basketball star
2. Teresa Weatherspoon's life story
3. how Teresa Weatherspoon is a symbol of change in sports

Test 3, page 26
1. why parents today have fewer serious conversations with their children
2. the benefits of male babysitters
3. why some parents choose homeschooling for their children

Finding the topic sentence

Test 1, page 27

1. e		3. d	
2. b		4. a	

Test 2, page 29

1. e		3. d	
2. c		4. a	

Test 3, page 31

1. c   3. a
2. e   4. b

Unit 6: Main Ideas

Stating the main idea

Any similar answer is acceptable.

Test 1, page 33

1. Topic: How people's negative ideas about wolves affected the wolves of North America
   Main Idea: The negative ideas people had about wolves is one reason why there are very few wolves left in North America.
2. Topic: What Native Americans knew about wolves
   Main Idea: Native Americans knew a lot more about wolves than most other Americans did.
3. Topic: The recent changes in Americans' thinking about wolves
   Main Idea: In the 1960s, Americans began to think about wolves in a different, more positive way.

Test 2, page 35

1. Topic: Damage caused by the Formosan termite in New Orleans
   Main Idea: The Formosan termite is causing a lot of damage in New Orleans.
2. Topic: How you can get Lyme disease from a deer tick bite
   Main Idea: Deer ticks in the woods can give you Lyme disease.
3. Topic: The harmless mites on our bodies
   Main Idea: In spite of our efforts to keep insects away from us, our bodies are covered with mites.

Test 3, page 37

1. Topic: The positive and negative effects of drinking coffee
   Main Idea: Drinking a moderate amount of coffee does not have any negative effects and may have some positive effects.
2. Topic: The history of the café in Europe in the twentieth century
   Main Idea: The café, which lost its popularity in the early twentieth century, became popular again towards the end of that century.
3. Topic: A university in Naples that teaches about coffee and cafés
   Main Idea: In Naples, a "Coffee University" offers courses about coffee and running a café.

Unit 7: Patterns of Organization

Recognizing patterns in sentences

Test 1, page 39

1. S *or* CE   6. CE
2. CE   7. CE *or* CC
3. L   8. L
4. CC *or* L   9. CE
5. S   10. CE

Test 2, page 40

1. CC   6. L
2. CE   7. CE
3. L   8. S
4. S   9. L
5. CC   10. L

Recognizing patterns in short passages

Test 1, page 41

1. Sentence c   Pattern S
2. Sentence e   Pattern CC
3. Sentence d   Pattern CE
4. Sentence a   Pattern L

Overall pattern   S

Test 2, page 43

1. Sentence b   Pattern S
2. Sentence e   Pattern CE
3. Sentence a   Pattern L
4. Sentence d   Pattern CC

Overall pattern   S

Test 3, page 45

1. Sentence d   Pattern S
2. Sentence e   Pattern L
3. Sentence c   Pattern CE
4. Sentence b   Pattern CC

Overall pattern   S

Unit 8: Skimming

Skimming encyclopedia entries

Test, page 47

1. A
2. B
3. B
4. Answers will vary.
5. B
6. Answers will vary.
7. *East of the Mountains of the Moon* or *The Chimpanzees of Gombe*
8. B
9. B
10. A

Unit 9: Making Inferences

Making inferences from short stories

Test 1, page 52
1. A man who is driving his car (the narrator) and a hitchhiker who is riding with him
2. In the narrator's car on the way to London
3. The hitchhiker took some things from the narrator.
4. Answers will vary.

Test 2, page 53
1. a young person, about 18 years old
2. The narrator's mother and father. He/she can't understand why they always have money problems; he/she feels sorry for them and wants to help them. At the same time, he/she thinks the problems were their own fault.
3. The father works in a jewelry shop.
4. The father went to a respected school—Cornell University—but has never been successful financially. Some of the father's old friends have been more successful. This is not the first time the parents have had financial problems. The mother had stopped being social for some time, but she was now becoming more involved in the community.
5. Answers will vary.

Test 3, page 54
1. Granny Weatherall, an old woman who is not very well and may be dying
2. in bed
3. Hapsy and Cornelia are her daughters. We don't know who Lydia and Jimmy are, but probably her other children, or her daughter and her husband. Doctor Harry is her doctor, and George is the man she loved 60 years ago.
4. Hapsy was probably her favorite daughter. Granny Weatherall was happily married and loved her family and her home. Now she wonders, though, if she missed something in her life—perhaps a different kind of love. That idea is represented by her memory of George, who left her and didn't marry her.
5. Answers will vary.

Inferring topics and main ideas

Test 1, page 56
1. tying your shoe
2. a car

Test 2, page 57
Any similar answers are acceptable.

1. a. The reviewer thinks that this is a good biography for the reader who wants a good account of Strauss's life. It is not a good biography for the reader who wants to know about the music that he wrote.
   b. It's stated in the last two lines of the passage.
2. a. The reviewer thinks this is a wonderful book for children and adults. It tells us a lot of interesting things about a famous writer's life, and it is very well written.
   b. It's stated in the first two lines and the last line of the passage.

Unit 10: Summarizing

Summarizing sentences

Any similar answers are acceptable.

Test 1, page 58
1. The Baskin family went to the ski lodge.
2. Jeff got ready to change a tire on his car.
3. The Hudson River is no longer polluted.
4. The school board president praised the high school students for winning many prizes.
5. Some scientists say that very bad weather may be caused by global warming.

Test 2, page 59
1. For their last English class, the students and teacher brought food from their own cultures.
2. You can find a lot of useful information with the computers in the college library.
3. Yoshi came into the house quietly.
4. The children cleaned up after dinner.
5. When he arrived in Brazil, John had to do many things to get settled there.

Summarizing short passages

Any similar answers are acceptable.

Test 1, page 60
1. Rain forests are important for people and for the planet.
2. Rain forests are being cut down and are disappearing all around the world.
3. The trees in northern rain forests are very old and grow slowly, so they cannot be replaced quickly.
4. Logging companies and environmentalists disagree about cutting down rain forests to make everyday products.

Summary: Rain forests are important for people and for the planet. They are being cut down, however, and are disappearing all around the world. Unfortunately, the trees in northern rain forests cannot be replaced quickly because they are very old and grow slowly. Logging companies and environmentalists disagree about cutting down rain forests to make everyday products.

Test 2, page 61

1. One way that a raven showed its intelligence was by stealing food from a zipped-up bag.
2. Two ravens tricked a dog and stole its food.
3. Some ravens have learned to stay warm by keeping streetlights turned on during the day.
4. Ravens can also say words and sound just like people.

Summary: Ravens show their intelligence in several ways. Some examples are stealing food from a zipped-up bag, and tricking a dog and stealing its food. Other ravens learned to stay warm by keeping streetlights turned on during the day. Ravens can even say words and sound just like people.

Test 3, page 62

1. As a young student, Harry Wu was put into prison for 19 years for disagreeing with the Chinese government.
2. Harry finished his education and moved to the United States to start a new life.
3. Harry was unable to forget the people still suffering in Chinese prisons, and he wanted to help them.
4. Harry Wu has made it his life's work to let the world know about the terrible conditions in Chinese prisons.

Summary: As a young student, Harry Wu was put into prison for 19 years for disagreeing with the Chinese government. After he got out of prison, he finished his education and moved to the United States. Once he arrived in America, though, he was unable to forget the people still suffering in Chinese prisons. He wanted to help them. Harry Wu has made it his life's work to let the world know about the terrible conditions in Chinese prisons.

Summarizing longer passages

Test 1, page 64
Step 3
    Part 1: Paragraph 1
    Part 2: Paragraphs 2–3
    Part 3: Paragraphs 4–6

Step 4
    Part 1: You can enjoy many water sports in Hawaii.
    Part 2: Surfing has a long history in Hawaii and requires great skill to do it well.
    Part 3: Scuba diving and snorkeling are great ways to get a close look at life under the surface of the ocean.

Step 5
You can enjoy many water sports in Hawaii. For example, surfing has a long history in Hawaii. Surfing requires great skill to do it well. Scuba diving and snorkeling, on the other hand, are great ways to get a close look at life under the surface of the ocean.

Test 2, page 66
Step 3
    Part 1: Paragraphs 1–3
    Part 2: Paragraphs 4–6
    Part 3: Paragraph 7
    Part 4: Paragraphs 8–9
Step 4
    Part 1: Jet lag results from air travel across multiple time zones, and the symptoms vary from person to person.
    Part 2: The three causes of jet lag are that people get tired getting ready for a trip, that they drink alcoholic beverages during the trip, and that their body's internal clocks are upset.
    Part 3: People who are less likely to feel the effects of jet lag are those who usually feel lively at night, younger people, and extroverts.
    Part 4: There is no real cure for jet lag, but travelers can overcome jet lag more quickly if they use several common sense strategies.
Step 5
Jet lag results from air travel across multiple time zones, and the symptoms vary from person to person. The three causes of jet lag are that people get tired getting ready for a trip, that they drink alcoholic beverages during the trip, and that their body's internal clock is upset. Not everyone feels the effects of jet lag, and those who are less likely to feel them are those who usually feel lively at night, younger people, and extroverts. While there is no real cure for jet lag, travelers can overcome jet lag more uickly if they use several common sense strategies.

Level One: **Evaluating Thinking Skills**

Test 1, page 69
1. c
2. a
3. d

4. b
5. c

Test 2, page 70
1. d
2. a
3. b

4. d
5. c

Test 3, page 71
1. b
2. d
3. a

4. a
5. c

Level Two: **Evaluating Thinking Skills**

Test 1, page 72
1. c
2. a
3. d

4. b
5. a

Test 2, page 73
1. c
2. a
3. d

4. c
5. c

Test 3, page 74
1. c
2. b
3. d

4. a
5. d

Level Three: **Evaluating Thinking Skills**

Test 1, page 76
1. b
2. a
3. d

4. d
5. a

Test 2, page 78
1. b
2. c
3. d

4. b
5. a

Test 3, page 80
1. d
2. c
3. a

4. c
5. c